PERPETUAL MOTION

Electrons and Atoms
in Crystals

ALEC T. STEWART, a Canadian, is Professor of Physics at the University of North Carolina, Chapel Hill, where he specializes in research on the behavior of electrons in crystals.

Born in 1925, in Saskatchewan, Stewart grew up in Nova Scotia, and attended Dalhousie University there. His first ambition, fostered by the building of model airplanes, was to become an aeronautical engineer, but, since Dalhousie offered no course in the subject, he took the B.Sc. degree (1946) in chemistry and physics and went on to study chemical engineering at Toronto. Switching back to physics, he received the M.Sc. degree (Dalhousie 1949) and then attended Cambridge University, England, on a scholarship. His work at Cambridge concerned measurement of fundamental forces between neutrons and protons. He received his Ph.D. in 1952.

On his return to Canada, Stewart joined a research group at the Chalk River Laboratories of Atomic Energy of Canada, Ltd., where he took part in the first extensive studies of the vibration of atoms as revealed in neutron-scattering experiments. He remained at Chalk River for five years and was Associate Professor of Physics at Dalhousie for three years before he joined the North Carolina faculty in 1960.

Professor Stewart has contributed many research articles to the several technical journals of physics.

PERPETUAL MOTION

Electrons and Atoms in Crystals

BY

ALEC T. STEWART

SCIENCE
STUDY
SERIES

Published by Anchor Books

Doubleday & Company, Inc.

Garden City, New York

Illustrations by
Mrs. Mary Scroggs and Kenneth E. Crook

The Science Study Series edition is
the first publication of *Perpetual Motion*

Library of Congress Catalog Card Number 64–19244

for
Professor H. L. Bronson
a teacher

THE SCIENCE STUDY SERIES

The Science Study Series offers to students and to the general public the writing of distinguished authors on the most stirring and fundamental topics of science, from the smallest known particles to the whole universe. Some of the books tell of the role of science in the world of man, his technology and civilization. Others are biographical in nature, telling the fascinating stories of the great discoverers and their discoveries. All the authors have been selected both for expertness in the fields they discuss and for ability to communicate their special knowledge and their own views in an interesting way. The primary purpose of these books is to provide a survey within the grasp of the young student or the layman. Many of the books, it is hoped, will encourage the reader to make his own investigations of natural phenomena.

The Series, which now offers topics in all the sciences and their applications, had its beginning in a project to revise the secondary schools' physics curriculum. At the Massachusetts Institute of Technology during 1956 a group of physicists, high school teachers, journalists, apparatus designers, film producers, and other specialists organized the Physical Science Study Committee, now operating as a part of Educational Services Incorporated, Watertown, Massachusetts. They pooled their knowledge and experience toward the design and creation of aids to the learning of physics. Initially their effort was supported by the National Science Foundation, which has continued to aid the program. The Ford Foundation, the Fund for the Advancement of Education, and the Alfred P. Sloan Foundation have also given support. The Committee has created a textbook, an extensive film series, a laboratory guide, especially designed apparatus, and a teacher's source book.

The Series is guided by a Board of Editors, consisting of Bruce F. Kingsbury, Managing Editor; John H. Durston, General Editor; Paul F. Brandwein, the Conservation Foundation and Harcourt, Brace & World, Inc.; Samuel A. Goudsmit, Brookhaven National Laboratory; Philippe Le-Corbeiller, Harvard University, and Gerard Piel, *Scientific American.*

ACKNOWLEDGMENTS

This little book has grown out of an earlier project planned with Dr. L. M. Slifkin, to whom, along with others in the Physics Department at Chapel Hill, I am grateful for comments and suggestions. The drawings have been made by Mrs. Mary Scroggs and Mr. Kenneth E. Crook. Mr. Bruce F. Kingsbury and Mr. John H. Durston have been helpful with critical comments. I am indebted to Atomic Energy of Canada, Ltd., for Plates XIII and XIV, to Arthur D. Little, Inc., for Plate XVI, and to the Physics Department of the University of North Carolina at Chapel Hill for all the remaining plates. To my wife, Alta K. Stewart, who typed repeatedly and who read critically, I am most indebted.

A. T. Stewart

Chapel Hill, 1964

CONTENTS

PERPETUAL MOTION

Electrons and Atoms
in Crystals

Chapter I

INTRODUCTION: IT CAN'T BE DONE

Leonardo da Vinci said it could not be done.

"O speculators about perpetual motion, how many vain chimeras have you created in the like quest? Go and take your place with the seekers after gold."

Nonetheless, for centuries inventors of all lands tried to build perpetual motion machines, but their contrivances never quite worked. Some of these inventions contained very clever mechanical ideas and the perpetual discussion created by the machine provided the inventor, his friends, and critics with stimulating entertainment.

As all scientists know, a machine that will run itself forever cannot be built. The basic difficulty is, of course, that all motion in the world of man involves some rubbing of one material over another. At the point of rubbing there are opposing forces which we call friction and these forces tend to stop the machine. Let us look at one of the simplest of such machines—a wheel and axle. If the wheel is very large and heavy and the bearings are exceptionally good, the wheel, once started, will continue spinning for a long time. Eventu-

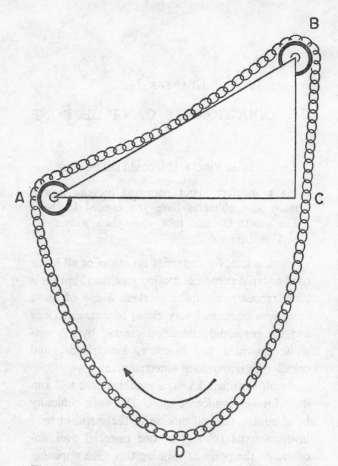

Fig. 1. Perpetual motion? When a uniform chain hangs over two pulleys, the weight of length *AD* equals the weight of *CD*. But since the weight of *AB* is greater than the weight of *BC*, the chain should run around anticlockwise gaining speed and producing energy. Why doesn't it?

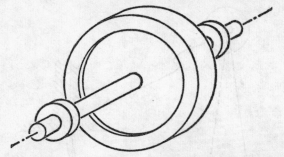

Fig. 2. A heavy wheel mounted on good bearings will continue to run for a long time on its own momentum but finally will stop.

ally, however, the friction at the bearings will slow the wheel down and finally will stop it.

Consider another perpetual motion machine, the pendulum, shown in Figure 3. The air friction on the ball and string can be removed by pumping the air away. The pendulum then hangs in a vacuum. But some friction will remain at the support where, within the string, one fiber rubs against another. If the pendulum were hung on a thread of quartz glass, one of the best materials for reducing this internal rubbing friction, the pendulum would swing for a very long time, but not perpetually.

There is another argument sometimes used by inventors of perpetual motion machines. They say that friction does not destroy the energy of motion but merely converts some of the mechanical kinetic energy into heat energy. This much is true. However, if these inventors then suggest that the heat energy can be converted back into

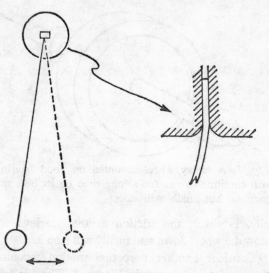

Fig. 3. Low internal friction of quartz fiber thread allows pendulum to swing for a long time.

mechanical energy to be returned to the machine, they lack understanding of one of the fundamental laws of heat engines. For reasons discussed elsewhere,[1] it turns out that no heat engine can ever be 100 percent efficient, even if friction losses are zero. Hence, inventors seem doomed to failure in attempts to make perpetual motion machines.

Yet to say that perpetual motion machines do not exist is false. On an atomic scale all nature is in perpetual motion. The air we breathe is made of fast-flying molecules moving in every direction, bouncing off one another and the walls,

[1] J. F. Sandfort, *Heat Engines* (Science Study Series S 27), Chapter 6.

never ceasing their random dance. These molecules live in a world without friction.[2] When oxygen and nitrogen molecules in the air around us bump into one another there is no loss of kinetic energy. After a collision they separate with the same total mechanical energy.

Not only in a gas are all molecules in perpetual motion. In a liquid and in a solid the atoms also are moving continually. In a liquid, atoms migrate from one place to another rapidly, but not, of

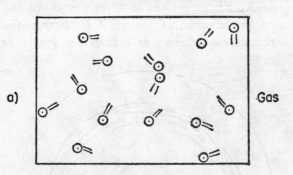

a)   Gas

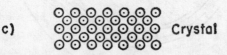

b)   Liquid

c)   Crystal

Fig. 4. The perpetual motion of atoms in nature. Even in a crystal the atoms never stop vibrating between their neighbors.

[2] See also the discussion in *Near Zero* by D. K. C. MacDonald (Science Study Series S 20), Chapter 1.

course, as fast as in a gas. In a solid there is just as much perpetual motion. Although it is customary to think of the atoms as fixed in position and not allowed to migrate, they vibrate fiercely about these fixed points.

In addition to the perpetual motion of the atoms and molecules flying about or vibrating in a crystal, each atom is itself a tiny perpetual motion machine with its cloud of electrons forever buzzing around the nucleus. These electrons experience no friction and so never slow down and stop. In an atom of sodium, for example, the electrons are arranged as indicated in Figure 5.

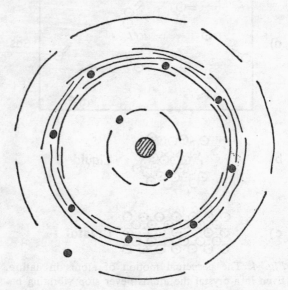

Fig. 5. The electrons in their various orbits in the sodium atom never stop.

Two of the electrons are moving around keeping very close to the nucleus. Farther out is a cloud of orbits of eight electrons. Beyond this cloud again is found the last and outermost electron of the sodium atom. In the smallest atom, hydrogen, there is only one electron, but in the large atoms there may be almost a hundred electrons—a large cloud of buzzing charges. They are all in ceaseless motion around the nucleus.

These, then, are nature's atomic perpetual motion machines: the atoms of which all matter is made and the electrons which swirl around the nucleus at the center of each atom.[3] In this book we examine the behavior of the atomic and electronic perpetual motion machines in the crystalline state of matter. We shall see that when atoms are arranged in rows, as they are in crystals, the vibrating motion of one atom affects its neighbors. They tend to vibrate together. This coupling together of many continuously moving atoms produces some interesting effects. Not only does the vibrational motion of one atom affect another when the atoms are close together, but the outer electrons influence one another profoundly. When the atoms are arranged in long rows, the behavior of these outer electrons is very remarkable. It accounts for almost all of the differences between soft and hard solids, between metals and nonmetals, and between colored and transparent

[3] In addition, all the constituent particles of the nucleus are in motion also. But that story belongs to the study of nuclear physics and will not be discussed here.

crystals. The resistance of metals to the passage of electrical current is a familiar phenomenon—it causes the wires of a toaster to glow red. In contrast to this is the surprising ability of some metals, when cold, to conduct electric current without any loss or resistance. This phenomenon, called superconductivity, is a large-scale manifestation of the perpetual motion of electrons.

In the chapters which follow we will discuss the sometimes startling and quite unexpected phenomena that occur in crystals. In large part the phenomena are due to the arranging in long rows, of millions of tiny perpetual motion machines. Some properties of crystals are much more amazing than even the dreams of perpetual motion inventors!

Chapter II

CRYSTALS AND STRUCTURES

1. *What Is a Crystal?*

Which materials are crystalline and which are not? A diamond or a sapphire is a crystal. A grain of sugar or of salt is a crystal. Plastic materials are not usually crystals. Glass is not a crystal. Even the expensive bowls called cut glass or crystal are not crystalline in the physicist's sense of the word. Mica is a crystal. So are the geologist's specimens of calcite, fluorite, and feldspar. All metals are crystalline.

What is a crystal? In the scientific sense of the word a crystal is any material in which atoms are arrayed in a repetitive pattern for distances

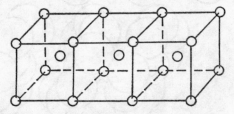

Fig. 6. The body-centered cubic crystal structure. Iron (Fe), sodium (Na), potassium (K), vanadium (V), molybdenum (Mo), and barium (Ba) crystallize in this body-centered cubic pattern.

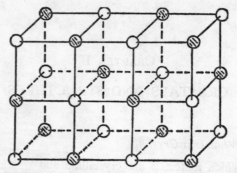

Fig. 7. The crystal structure of common salt (NaCl). Many other compounds have this structure—for example, sodium fluoride (NaF), lithium chloride (LiCl), and magnesium oxide (MgO).

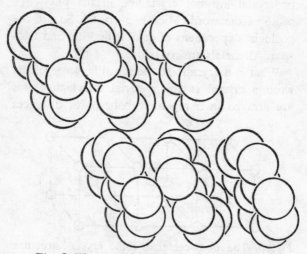

Fig. 8. The crystal structure of naphthalene.

of hundreds, thousands, even millions of atomic spacings. The particular arrangement of atoms along the line does not matter as long as the arrangement repeats itself very many times. In iron the atoms are equally spaced along a line that is one edge of a repeating cube, as indicated in Figure 6. In salt (Figure 7), sodium and chlorine

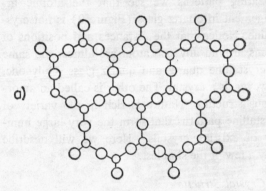

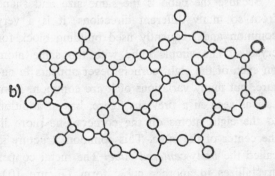

Fig. 9. Crystalline (a) and fused (b) quartz. The small circles represent silicon (Si) atoms and the large ones oxygen (O) atoms.

ions alternate on the corners of the cube. A crystal of naphthalene is drawn in Figure 8. Here we see that the pattern repeats after every two complete molecules of naphthalene, each of which contains many atoms. But all these meet the basic condition for being a crystal. *Some atomic pattern repeats itself many times.* In contrast to these repeating patterns we see that the atomic arrangement in quartz glass (Figure 9) is not crystalline. Notice that the distances and positions of atoms around any one atom are almost the same in crystalline quartz and quartz glass. Only one, however, is a crystal. The other is called an amorphous structure. Nature is rich in the variety of crystalline patterns that form the very large number of existing crystals.[1] Here we will describe only a few of the simplest.

2. *Crystal Structure*

Because the cube is the same size and shape from so many different directions, it is a very common and frequently used building block for crystals. The simple cube with the same atom on each of the eight corners never appears in nature, but many variations of it are common. Iron, as was seen in a previous figure, has in addition to the eight atoms on the corners one more in the center of the cube. This common structure is called the *body-centered cube*. The metal copper crystallizes in another cubic form (Figure 10).

[1] See *Crystals and Crystal Growing* by Alan Holden and Phylis Singer (Science Study Series S 7).

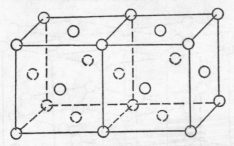

Fig. 10. The crystal structure of copper (Cu). The face-centered cubic structure also describes crystals of silver (Ag), aluminum (Al), gold (Au), lead (Pb), platinum (Pt), and other metals.

It has, in addition to the eight atoms on the corners, six more atoms in the center of each of the six faces of the cube. This structure is called the *face-centered cube.* The very important industrial metal zinc, used in casting type and in many small parts of machines, crystallizes in an interesting pattern based on the hexagon. It is simplest to view (Figure 11) as a series of planes, each containing hexagonal nets of atoms stacked one above the other with every second plane shifted slightly in one direction. The amount of shift is just enough to make the atoms in one plane come directly over, and under, the center of one of the equilateral triangles of the hexagon in the plane below. This is a structure somewhat complicated to describe, but it is surprisingly like the face-centered cube. The crystalline structure of zinc is called *hexagonal close-packed.* It is one of the two possible arrangements giving the densest packing

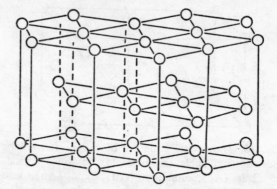

Fig. 11. Crystal structure of zinc (Zn), magnesium (Mg), beryllium (Be), cadmium (Cd), and many other metals crystallize with the hexagonal close-packed structure.

of hard spheres. The other dense structure is the face-centered cubic already described. It resembles the hexagonal close-packed when viewed along the diagonal passing from one corner through the center of the cube to the opposite corner. A fourth important crystal structure is the *diamond structure.* Diamond, as well as silicon and germanium, the elements used in transistors, has the structure shown in Figure 12. It is easiest to describe as two separate face-centered lattices or networks penetrating one another.

Most elements crystallize in one of these four simple structures—the body-centered cube, the face-centered cube, hexagonal close-packed or the diamond structure. The more complex crystalline compounds, however, have many different patterns. Only one will be mentioned at this time, and this one because of its simplicity. This is the

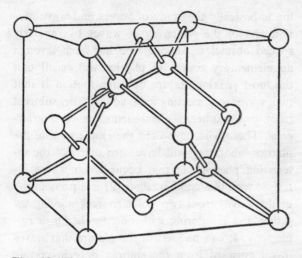

Fig. 12. The crystal structure of diamond, silicon (Si), and germanium (Ge).

structure of common table salt, sodium chloride. The sodium and chlorine atoms together form a simple cube with unlike atoms next to one another, as we have seen in Figure 7. Notice that this structure can also be described as two interpenetrating face-centered cubic lattices, one of sodium atoms and the other of chlorine atoms. Most of our knowledge of the behavior of the perpetually moving electrons and atoms in crystals has been obtained by study of such simple structures.

3. X-ray Scattering by Crystals

X-rays have proved to be the most useful tool for determining the atomic arrangements of crystals found in nature. The study of X-ray scattering is basically the study of waves and wave motion and of the scattering of waves by regularly spaced obstacles. Anyone who has been through an elementary course in physics will recall that the most striking feature of wave motion is that two waves on meeting can add to, or subtract from, one another, a phenomenon called *interference*. Those who have used the ripple tank in the physics laboratory will have seen many of the interesting phenomena that occur when waves interfere with one another. Plate VI is a photograph of the waves from two point sources moving together and interfering with one another in a ripple tank. It can be seen in the picture that waves travel outward from the sources only in certain directions and that between these directions there is no wave motion. If there were more sources equally spaced in a line with the two shown, the regions of outward wave travel would be narrower and the in-between quiet regions broader. The same result would be obtained if the sources in the tank were replaced with a set of fixed posts and waves from a single far-distant source were scattered from them. This is the phenomenon called *diffraction*. It occurs when water waves hit the piles of a pier, when light waves are passed through a fine screen, and when X-rays are scattered by the regularly spaced atoms of a crystal. The most familiar example of diffraction in light waves is the cross you see when you look at a distant streetlamp through a window screen. All these diffraction patterns occur because waves can add to one another and subtract from one another.

Interesting diffraction patterns result when the length of the waves (that is, the distance from one wave crest to the next) is about the same as the spacing between posts. It is easy to estimate this distance between "posts," the atoms, in a solid. From Avogadro's Number[2] and the atomic weight of copper, for example, it is known that one atom of copper weighs:

$$\frac{63.6 \text{ gms}}{6.02 \times 10^{23}} = 1.06 \times 10^{-22} \text{ gms.}[3]$$

The density of copper is 8.9 grams per cubic centimeter, or 8.9 gm/cm^3. Thus the number of atoms per centimeter cube is:

$$\frac{8.9 \text{ gm/cm}^3}{1.06 \ 10^{-22} \text{ gm/atom}} = 8.4 \ 10^{22} \frac{\text{atoms}}{\text{cm}^3}$$

The number of atoms along one edge of a centimeter cube will be of the order of the cube root of this number; that is, about 4.4×10^7. Hence, the distance between near atoms is the reciprocal

[2] Avogadro's Number is 6.02×10^{23}. It is the number of atoms of a substance in a mass whose weight in grams is numerically equal to its relative atomic weight. Thus, 6.02×10^{23} is the number of atoms of hydrogen in 1 gm of H_2, the number of atoms of oxygen in 16 gms of O_2, and the number of atoms of any element in one gram atom of that element. Thus 63.6 gms of copper contain 6.02×10^{23} copper atoms.

[3] In the notation of *orders of magnitude* 10^2 means 100, 10^3 means 1000, 10^{23} means 100,000,000,000,000,000,-000,000, 10^{-22} means 1/10,000,000,000,000,000,000,000.

of this number, about 2.3×10^{-8} cm. Thus, when a solid is irradiated with waves of approximately this wavelength one should expect to see interference effects. X-rays, discovered just before the start of this century, were thought to have a wavelength of this size. If so, and if atoms were arranged in rows in crystals, then one should be able to observe some sort of interference effect in the scattering of X-rays by crystals. The German physicist Max von Laue made this prediction in 1912 and with his colleagues W. Friedrich

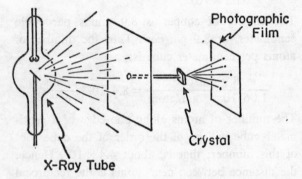

Fig. 13. The standard arrangement of apparatus for photographing diffracted X-rays. On passing through the crystal the rays are scattered into a pattern recorded on the film. The developed film is a "picture" similar to *Plate VII.*

and P. Knipping quickly verified it. Their experimental arrangement is shown in the diagram of Figure 13; their photographic results were similar to those in Plate VII. This picture shows that the X-rays were scattered in certain directions just as were the water waves in the ripple tank. Professor W. L. Bragg, at Cambridge University, in 1912, proposed a simple way of understanding these particular directions. His explanation can be followed from Figure 14.

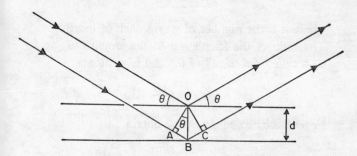

Fig. 14. Reflection of X-rays. The ray scattered by the lower plane at *B* must travel the extra distance *ABC*. If this distance is some number of whole wavelengths the ray will be in step with, and thus able to add to, the upper ray.

The two horizontal lines in the drawing represent two planes containing atoms in the crystal. There are more such planes above and below the ones drawn, but the argument need concern only one pair of adjacent planes. It is supposed that all the atoms are in these planes and none in between them. Two parallel rays are shown striking the crystal, the lower one being reflected from the second plane at point B. Both waves make the same angle θ (theta) with the atomic planes. If the waves scattered from the crystal planes are to add up, or reinforce one another, the difference between the path lengths of these two waves must be some whole number of wavelengths. This path length difference is the length ABC, or $2\,AB$. The condition for the waves to add up may be written

$$nL = 2\,AB$$

where n is the number of waves each of length L. The ratio of the length AB to the length OB, or d, is called the "sine" of θ,[4] and is written

$$\sin\,\theta = \frac{AB}{d}$$

From these two equations we obtain

$$nL = 2d\,\sin\,\theta$$

This relation between the whole number n (which may be any whole number but is usually a small one), the wavelength L, the spacing between the planes d, and the angle of the X-ray beam, is

[4] The trigonometric ratios are based on the sides of a right-angled triangle, but hold under all conditions for any given angle. They have many applications in every phase of technology and engineering and are of great importance in higher mathematics.

a/c is called the sine of θ and is written $\sin\,\theta = a/c$.
b/c is called the cosine of θ and is written $\cos\,\theta = b/c$.
a/b is called the tangent of θ and is written $\tan\,\theta = a/b$.

known as Bragg's Law of X-ray reflection. By measuring the angles of X-ray scattering one can obtain the distances between the atoms in a crystal with great precision, actually to better than one ten-billionth of an inch! The theory and practice of X-ray diffraction has been much improved since those early days, and now one can determine the structure of very complicated crystals. The structure of a small section of a protein molecular structure so determined is shown in the model in Plate VIII.

4. *Diffraction of Other Waves and Particles*

Since the discovery of X-ray diffraction even more startling diffraction effects have been observed. In 1924 Louis de Broglie made the very bold speculation that small particles of matter might be treated as waves for certain purposes. He suggested that beams of particles might be diffracted just as X-rays are. Three years later, partly by accident, Clinton J. Davisson and L. H. Germer, working at the Bell Laboratories, observed that this was so. They were experimenting with reflected beams of electrons and inadvertently heated a nickel reflector until it formed larger single crystals. When this piece of nickel produced strange reflections Davisson and Germer experimented with a single crystal of nickel and observed directly for the first time the diffraction of "waves" of matter. This startling observation is now fully described in terms of a wave theory of matter, which was developed following de Broglie's suggestion. The mechanics of matter waves, or "wave mechanics" as it is called, was developed first, in the 1920s and 30s, by Erwin Schroedinger, Max Born, Werner Heisenberg, and Paul A. M. Dirac. Although discovered many years ago, diffracted beams of electrons are only now being used extensively as a tool for the study of solids. But since beams of electrons penetrate very slightly into matter, they are used primarily for the study of surfaces.

More recently the development of nuclear reactors has provided physicists and chemists with intense beams of neutrons which, like beams of X-rays, electrons, or any other particles, have wave properties. Neutrons also are diffracted by crystals and can provide information about the positions of atoms in the crystal, just as X-rays do. Neutrons have certain advantages over X-rays when the information sought is not so much the location of atoms in the crystal but instead the vigor with which the atoms are vibrating. Neutrons have as well the interesting property of being magnetic. They behave like very small bar magnets. Thus neutron diffraction can distinguish between atoms that are magnetic and those that are nonmagnetic. Using neutrons, physicists have learned that in some crystals the atoms are magnetized parallel to one another and in others they are antiparallel; that is, alternate magnets point in opposite directions.

The operation of a neutron diffraction apparatus is illustrated in the schematic drawing of Figure 15a. Neutrons from a reactor are scattered by a single crystal at A. Those neutrons with the correct wavelength will be reflected as a beam in the direction of the specimen. Since the wave-

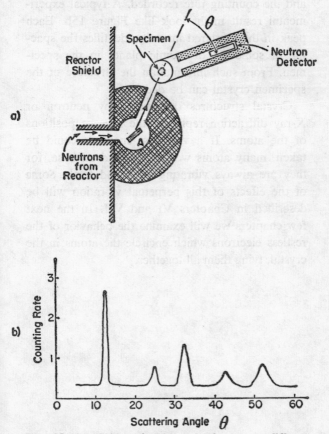

Fig. 15. (a) Schematic diagram of neutron diffraction apparatus. (b) Plot of the neutron counting rate in detector against the scattering angle, θ.

length of this selected beam of neutrons is known, it can be used to measure the spacing between planes of atoms in the specimen. The neutron counter is swung in an arc around the specimen and the counting rate recorded. A typical experimental result might look like Figure 15b. Each peak in the scattered intensity identifies the spacing of some set of atomic planes in the specimen. From such information the structure of the specimen crystal can be deduced.

Crystal structures determined by neutron or X-ray diffraction represent the average positions of the atoms. If a very fast snapshot could be taken, many atoms would be found off-base, for they are always vibrating back and forth. Some of the effects of this perpetual vibration will be described in Chapters VI and VII. In the next few chapters we will examine the behavior of the restless electrons which encircle the atoms in the crystal, tying them all together.

CHAPTER III

ELECTRONS IN
NONMETALLIC CRYSTALS

1. *Electrons in Atoms*

Hydrogen is the simplest element. It has only one electron flying around the nucleus, which carries a single positive charge. After hydrogen comes helium with two electrons and a nuclear charge of plus two to compensate. If a nucleus has three positive charges, three electrons will gather around, and we have a lithium atom; if four positive charges, beryllium; five, boron, and so on.

The complete list of elements with name and symbol is shown in Table I. Dimitri Ivanovich Mendeleev, in 1869, arranged this list in a table in which the elements in columns had similar chemical properties. Figure 16 shows such a tabulation. One of the most startling properties of atoms can be seen from this table. Atoms with certain numbers of electrons are virtually inert to chemical reaction. Helium does not react. Eight elements further in the list comes neon, which is also inert; then after eight more elements, argon. Further on in the Periodic Table

Periodic Table of the Elements

TYPE →	R_2O / RH	RO / RH_2	R_2O_3	RO_2	R_2O_5	RO_3	R_2O_7		RO_4		R_2O	RO	R_2O_3	RO_2 / H_4R	R_2O_5 / H_3R	RO_3 / H_2R	R_2O_7 / HR	INERT GASES
GROUP →	IA	IIA	IIIB	IVB	VB	VIB	VIIB	VIIIB			IB	IIB	IIIA	IVA	VA	VIA	VIIA	VIIIA
PERIOD 1	1 H HYDROGEN 1·0080																	2 He HELIUM 4·003
PERIOD 2	3 Li LITHIUM 6·940	4 Be BERYLLIUM 9·013											5 B BORON 10·82	6 C CARBON 12·011	7 N NITROGEN 14·008	8 O OXYGEN 16·000	9 F FLUORINE 19·000	10 Ne NEON 20·183
PERIOD 3	11 Na SODIUM 22·991	12 Mg MAGNESIUM 24·32											13 Al ALUMINIUM 26·98	14 Si SILICON 28·09	15 P PHOSPHORUS 30·975	16 S SULFUR 32·066	17 Cl CHLORINE 35·457	18 A ARGON 39·944
PERIOD 4	19 K POTASSIUM 39·100	20 Ca CALCIUM 40·08	21 Sc SCANDIUM 45·10	22 Ti TITANIUM 47·90	23 V VANADIUM 50·95	24 Cr CHROMIUM 52·01	25 Mn MANGANESE 54·94	26 Fe IRON 55·85	27 Co COBALT 58·94	28 Ni NICKEL 58·71	29 Cu COPPER 63·54	30 Zn ZINC 65·38	31 Ga GALLIUM 69·72	32 Ge GERMANIUM 72·60	33 As ARSENIC 74·91	34 Se SELENIUM 78·96	35 Br BROMINE 79·916	36 Kr KRYPTON 83·80
PERIOD 5	37 Rb RUBIDIUM 85·48	38 Sr STRONTIUM 87·63	39 Y YTTRIUM 88·92	40 Zr ZIRCONIUM 91·22	41 Nb NIOBIUM 92·91	42 Mo MOLYBDENUM 95·95	43 Tc TECHNETIUM (99)	44 Ru RUTHENIUM 101·1	45 Rh RHODIUM 102·91	46 Pd PALLADIUM 106·7	47 Ag SILVER 107·880	48 Cd CADMIUM 112·41	49 In INDIUM 114·76	50 Sn TIN 118·70	51 Sb ANTIMONY 121·76	52 Te TELLURIUM 127·61	53 I IODINE 126·91	54 Xe XENON 131·3
PERIOD 6	55 Cs CESIUM 132·91	56 Ba BARIUM 137·36	57–71 *	72 Hf HAFNIUM 178·58	73 Ta TANTALUM 180·95	74 W WOLFRAM 183·86	75 Re RHENIUM 186·22	76 Os OSMIUM 190·2	77 Ir IRIDIUM 192·2	78 Pt PLATINUM 195·23	79 Au GOLD 197·0	80 Hg MERCURY 200·61	81 Tl THALLIUM 204·39	82 Pb LEAD 207·21	83 Bi BISMUTH 209·00	84 Po POLONIUM 209–210	85 At ASTATINE (211·)	86 Rn RADON 222·
PERIOD 7	87 Fr FRANCIUM (223)	88 Ra RADIUM 226·05	89–98 **															

LIGHT METALS · HEAVY METALS · NONMETALS

RARE EARTH ELEMENTS

* LANTHANIDE SERIES

57 La LANTHANUM 138·92	58 Ce CERIUM 140·13	59 Pr PRASEODYMIUM 140·92	60 Nd NEODYMIUM 144·27	61 Pm PROMETHIUM (145)	62 Sm SAMARIUM 150·35	63 Eu EUROPIUM 152·0	64 Gd GADOLINIUM 156·9	65 Tb TERBIUM 158·93	66 Dy DYSPROSIUM 162·51	67 Ho HOLMIUM 164·94	68 Er ERBIUM 167·27	69 Tm THULIUM 168·94	70 Yb YTTERBIUM 173·04	71 Lu LUTETIUM 174·99

** ACTINIDE SERIES

89 Ac ACTINIUM 227·0	90 Th THORIUM 232·05	91 Pa PROTACTINIUM 231·	92 U URANIUM 238·07	93 Np NEPTUNIUM (237)	94 Pu PLUTONIUM (242)	95 Am AMERICIUM (243)	96 Cm CURIUM (245)	97 Bk BERKELIUM (249)	98 Cf CALIFORNIUM (249)	99 E EINSTEINIUM (254)	100 Fm FERMIUM (252)	101 Mv MENDELEVIUM (256)	102 No NOBELIUM —

Fig. 16. Periodic Table of the elements.

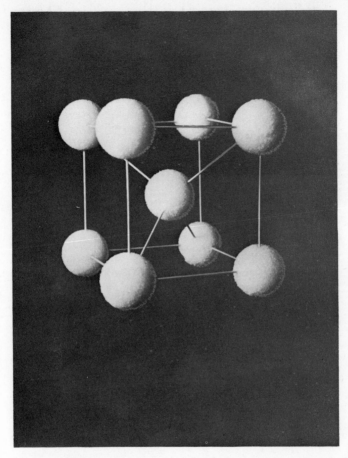

PLATE I. Model of body-centered cubic structure possessed by iron and many other metals. See *Fig. 6*.

PLATE II. Model of the crystal structure of common salt (NaCl). See *Fig. 7.*

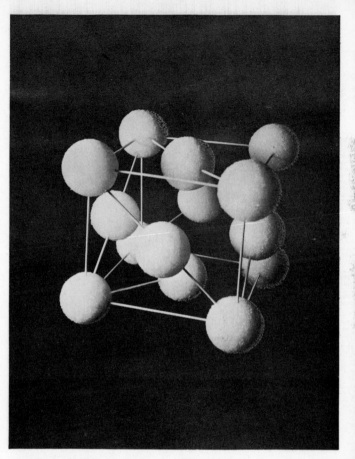

PLATE III. The face-centered cubic structure of copper (Cu) and many other metals. See *Fig. 10.*

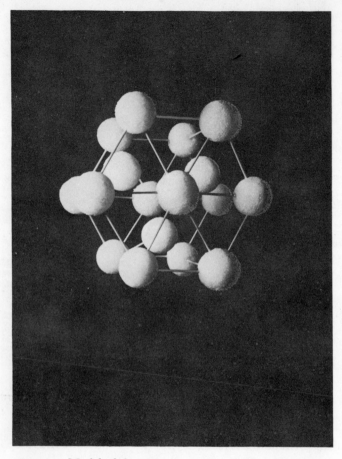

PLATE IV. Model of the crystal structure of zinc, called hexagonal close-packed. See *Fig. 11*.

PLATE V. The crystal structure of diamond is shown in this model. The vertical direction in this model is the direction of a diagonal through the center of the cube of *Fig. 12*.

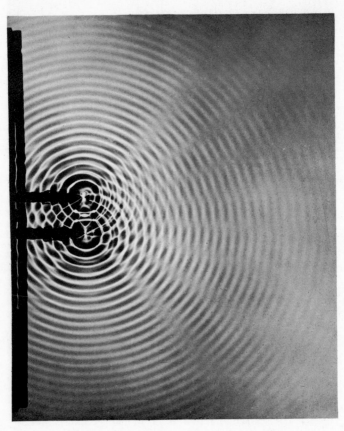

PLATE VI. Interference of waves from two sources.

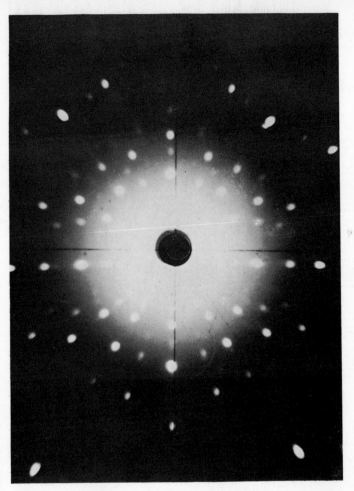

PLATE VII. An X-ray crystal "photograph" taken by the method shown in *Fig. 13*.

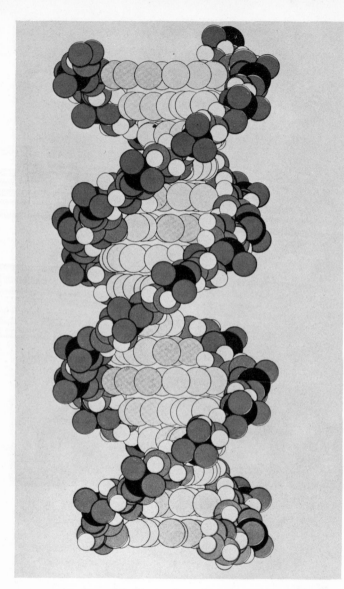

PLATE VIII. A model of a small section of a protein molecule.

come krypton and zenon.[1] These elements are unique in the Periodic Table in that they react with no other atoms.[2] The number eight is very important to the electrons in the atom. If eight electrons get together in a shell around the nucleus of an atom they are completely content and

TABLE I
LIST OF ELEMENTS

Atomic Number	Symbol	Name
1	H	Hydrogen
2	He	Helium
3	Li	Lithium
4	Be	Beryllium
5	B	Boron
6	C	Carbon
7	N	Nitrogen
8	O	Oxygen
9	F	Fluorine
10	Ne	Neon
11	Na	Sodium
12	Mg	Magnesium
13	Al	Aluminum
14	Si	Silicon
15	P	Phosphorus
16	S	Sulfur
17	Cl	Chlorine

[1] As students of chemistry will realize, there are other numbers besides eight (for example, eighteen or thirty-two) which give completed inner shells in larger atoms. Eight electrons, however, always give a stable shell and a rare gas atom. So do two electrons in the one case of the helium atom.

[2] In the most favorable circumstances some reactions are possible. For example, fluorine, which attracts electrons most strongly, can cause some of the "inert" gases to react.

TABLE I (Continued)

Atomic Number	Symbol	Name
18	A	Argon
19	K	Potassium
20	Ca	Calcium
21	Sc	Scandium
22	Ti	Titanium
23	V	Vanadium
24	Cr	Chromium
25	Mn	Manganese
26	Fe	Iron
27	Co	Cobalt
28	Ni	Nickel
29	Cu	Copper
30	Zn	Zinc
31	Ga	Galium
32	Ge	Germanium
33	As	Arsenic
34	Se	Selenium
35	Br	Bromine
36	Kr	Krypton
37	Rb	Rubidium
38	Sr	Strontium
39	Y	Yttrium
40	Zr	Zirconium
41	Nb	Niobium
42	Mo	Molybdenum
43	Tc	Technetium
44	Ru	Ruthenium
45	Rh	Rhodium
46	Pd	Palladium
47	Ag	Silver
48	Cd	Cadmium
49	In	Indium
50	Sn	Tin
51	Sb	Antimony
52	Te	Tellurium
53	I	Iodine
54	Xe	Xenon
55	Cs	Cesium
56	Ba	Barium

57	La	Lanthanum
58	Ce	Cerium
59	Pr	Praseodymium
60	Nd	Neodymium
61	Pm	Promethium
62	Sm	Samarium
63	Eu	Europium
64	Gd	Gadolinium
65	Tb	Terbium
66	Dy	Dysprosium
67	No	Holmium
68	Er	Erbium
69	Tm	Thulium
70	Yb	Ytterbium
71	Lu	Lutecium
72	Hf	Hafnium
73	Ta	Tantalum
74	W	Tungsten
75	Re	Rhenium
76	Os	Osmium
77	Ir	Iridium
78	Pt	Platinum
79	Au	Gold
80	Hg	Mercury
81	Tl	Thallium
82	Pb	Lead
83	Bi	Bismuth
84	Po	Polonium
85	At	Astatine
86	Rn	Radon
87	Fr	Francium
88	Ra	Radium
89	Ac	Actinium
90	Th	Thorium
91	Pa	Protoactinium
92	U	Uranium

unreactive, and much prefer to remain undisturbed. On the other hand, if there are only seven electrons, as in fluorine, chlorine, bromine, and iodine, the group is not quite complete (Figure

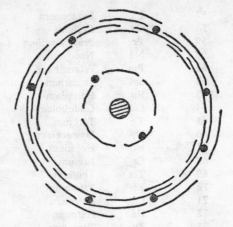

Fig. 17. Fluorine atom. If one more electron were added to the outer shell to make a fluoride ion (F⁻), the atom would then have a filled outer shell of eight electrons and be very stable.

17). These atoms are very reactive. They will do their best to capture another electron from any atom nearby in order to complete the shell. Elements such as oxygen, with two electrons missing, similarly try to capture two electrons from atoms near them and are therefore reactive chemically. However, the capture of two electrons is harder than the capture of one. Therefore oxygen is not as reactive as fluorine.

At the other side of the Periodic Chart lie elements with one electron more than the stable set of eight. These are the elements lithium, sodium, potassium, rubidium, and cesium. (Sodium is shown in the schematic diagram of Figure 5.) The extra, outermost electron possessed by each

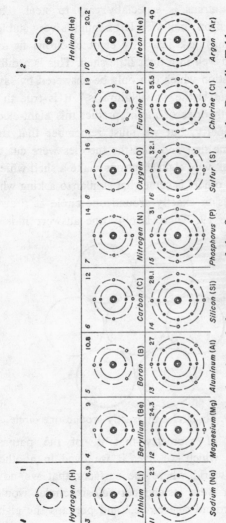

Fig. 18. Schematic drawing of the atoms of the first two rows of the Periodic Table (from *Scientific American*, January 1963).

of these atoms is especially easy to steal. The eight-electron shell then left behind is very stable.

One may ask just why eight electrons fit together so well in a tight little shell. This is a difficult question which can only be answered by saying, "That is the way Nature is." It is true that modern theories of atoms predict this eight-electron property, but we must remember that the facts came first and that the theories were cut to fit. To ask why eight electrons make a shell which excludes others is somewhat similar to asking why six circles fit exactly around one circle as drawn in Figure 19. There is only one answer: it is a

Fig. 19. Six circles fit exactly around one circle.

property of geometry—that is, of the natural world in which we live. If we lived in another kind of world where the surfaces that we now think flat were instead curved, six circles would not fit around one circle,[3] and perhaps the eight

[3] Try to fit six nickels around one nickel on the surface of a globe.

electrons that make a stable shell in our world might not be stable in this other world. At any rate, in our world all chemistry (and even all biological life) is based in part upon the tendency of electrons to form stable shells of eight around the nucleus of atoms.

How is information obtained about the electrons swarming around the nucleus of an atom? The magnitude of the positive charge of the nucleus, and hence the number of electrons, can be obtained by scattering experiments in which high-speed particles are bounced off nuclei and the number deflected at various angles is determined. These experiments were first done by Hans Geiger and E. Marsden with Lord Rutherford[4] about 1910, and are best discussed in books on nuclear physics. Nowadays, the charge on the nucleus is not often obtained by scattering, but rather through the use of X-rays. When an electron changes from one orbit to another orbit closer to the nucleus it gives up energy as X-rays. The nuclear charge may be calculated from the energy of this X-ray.

The approximate size of atoms can be obtained easily from the density of solids if we assume that in the densest solids atoms are just about touching one another. This and other techniques tell us that atoms are about one or two Ångströms in diameter, an Ångström unit being 10^{-8} centimeter.

[4] See *Rutherford and the Nature of the Atom*, by E. N. da C. Andrade (Science Study Series S 35).

It is more difficult to determine how fast an electron is moving. We can't time an electron over a fixed course as we might a racing car, nor can we take successive photographs and compare them. The atom is such a tiny and delicate system that all our normal techniques for measuring speed are much too cumbersome. Perhaps the most gentle method of searching for an electron in an atom (in order to measure its speed) is to shoot another electron through the atom. If the exploring electron hits an electron in the atom, it is deflected, and from the angle it may be possible to obtain the velocity of the electron it hit. But from the atom's point of view this technique is not exactly subtle; it would be like closing one's eyes and driving full speed through a street intersection to find out whether traffic was moving on the cross street. If a collision occurred, one could assume that there was a car on the cross street. Unfortunately there is no more delicate way of observing electrons in their orbits.

Since the days of Rutherford a very great amount of information about electrons in atoms has been collected, and the theory of electron behavior in atoms has been well worked out. The drawings in Figures 5, 17, and 18 are only schematic and should not be taken as an accurate description of the atoms. Indeed, if we actually could see an atom of sodium, for example, it might look more like Figure 20 than the previous figures. Here can be distinguished the small inner shell of two electrons, the complete shell of eight

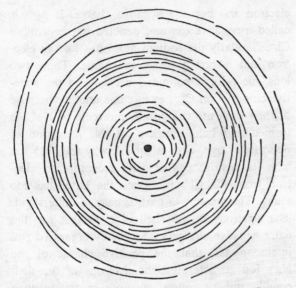

Fig. 20. A more realistic suggestion of the configuration of the sodium atom.

electrons, and the wispy haze of the final outer electron wandering around by itself. The electrons are moving so fast (about 10^{16} orbits per second) that they would appear only as a blur. This motion is not only perpetual but very fast.

2. Crystals of Ions

How are chemical compounds formed? Suppose a chlorine atom and a sodium atom bumped together. Immediately the outer spare electron of the sodium atom would be seized by the chlorine atom to complete its shell of eight. Notice what has happened. The chlorine atom has gained an electron and hence a negative charge. It now is called a negative *ion* and denoted by the symbol Cl^-. Similarly the sodium atom has lost an electron and is now positive in charge. These two ions, the positive sodium ion Na^+ and the negative chlorine ion Cl^-, attract one another because of their opposite charges. A molecule of NaCl is formed and held together by this attraction of opposite charge. One might ask why the Na^+ ion with its positive charge can't recapture an electron from the Cl^- ion since the latter has too many. The answer, in part, is easy to understand. The electrons of the shell of eight that has the extra negative charge are so tightly organized and interconnected that the positive charge of the Na^+ ion attracts all eight electrons of the shell equally and, of course, succeeds in getting none at all. In spite of the extra negative charge of the Cl^- ion, the shell of eight electrons is so well interconnected that it can keep its extra electron from jumping back to the Na^+ ion.

In a solid the positive sodium ion gathers many negative chlorine ions around it, and the chlorine ion similarly gathers many sodium ions. A crystal structure is formed with six positive ions around each negative ion and six negative ions around each positive ion. This crystal structure we have seen already, in Figure 7 of Chapter II. This kind of solid is called an *ionic crystal,* for it is a crystal of ions, not atoms. Almost all of the alkali metals, lithium, sodium, potassium, rubidium, cesium, combine with the halogens, the elements fluorine, chlorine, bromine, and iodine, to form this type of structure, held together only by the attraction between opposite charges. Many other atoms can form ionic crystals. An oxygen atom and a magnesium atom may exchange two electrons to form the positive magnesium ion, Mg^{++}, and the negative oxygen ion, O^{--}. These two form a single molecule of MgO, magnesium oxide. The crystal structure is similar to that of NaCl.

Other types of ionic crystals are also possible

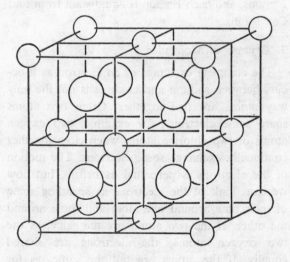

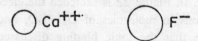

$\bigcirc$ Ca^{++} $\bigcirc$ F$^-$

Fig. 21. The crystal structure of fluorite (CaF$_2$).

when the charges of the two types of ions are not the same. The beautiful crystal fluorite (Plate IX) is made up of Ca^{++} ions, all doubly charged from having lost two electrons, and fluoride ions, F^-, singly charged from one extra electron. Since there must be twice as many fluoride ions as calcium ions the formula is CaF_2. The crystal structure (Figure 21) is different from NaCl. In this structure, as in the NaCl structure, no particular atoms can be associated with one another to form CaF_2. Each Ca^{++} ion is equidistant from eight F^- ions, and each F^- ion is equidistant from four Ca^{++} ions.

3. *Crystals of Molecules*

The complete exchange of an electron as it occurs between sodium and chlorine is not the only way atoms are tied together. Often two atoms share some electrons; for example, two oxygen atoms or two chlorine atoms when close together continually exchange some electrons. The motion of the electrons is perpetual as before, but now we can think of the electrons as spending some of their time around one atom and some around the other. If the two atoms are the same, as the two oxygen atoms, the electrons are shared equally. If the atoms are not the same, as for example, in water, H_2O, the electrons are not shared equally. In Figure 22 is sketched the electron distributions in molecules of O_2, H_2O, and NaCl. We see that the ionic binding discussed previously is the extreme situation of the unequal

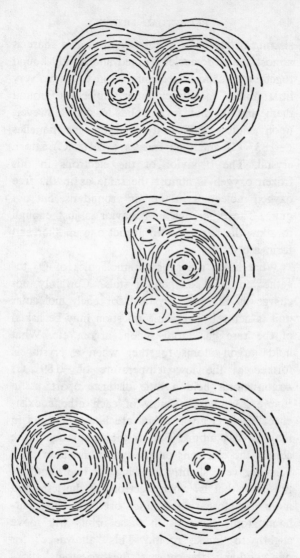

Fig. 22. Molecules of oxygen (O₂), water (H₂O), and salt (NaCl), from top to bottom.

sharing of electrons. The sodium atom's share is almost zero. Molecules formed and tightly bound together by shared electrons, as in O_2, have very little ability to attract other molecules around them and do not form solids easily. However, upon cooling sufficiently, oxygen gas liquefies ($-183°$ C) and then freezes ($-218°$ C) into a crystal. The behavior of the electrons in this frozen oxygen is almost the same as in the free oxygen molecules in the air around us, but not quite. The difference in behavior is just enough to allow the molecules to attract one another and form a crystal.

What holds the separate molecules of O_2 together in solid oxygen crystals? Certainly not charge as in ionic crystals, for each molecular unit is neutral. The same question may be asked of the rare gas atoms neon, argon, etc. What holds argon atoms together when a crystal is formed at the low temperature of $-189°$ C? Argon atoms held a little distance apart, as in Figure 23a, hardly know of each other's existence. Their electron orbits are like the orbits in the free gas atoms. But as they approach more closely the electrons on the two atoms alter their behavior very slightly allowing for one another's presence; that is, when electrons of the left-hand atom are close to the outer orbits of the right-hand atom, electrons in these orbits will move slightly to "make room." This "allowance" for one another is the cause of the two atoms' sticking together. In the situation in (b) the atom on

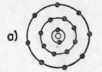

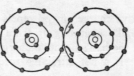

Fig. 23. (a) Two argon atoms far apart feel no attraction. (b) When the argon atoms are closer together the electrons of the two different atoms may modify their orbits briefly and cause a weak attraction.

the left appears to the atom on the right to be slightly negatively charged, and vice versa. These two very small opposite apparent charges attract one another. A moment later the situation may be reversed, but the atoms still attract one another. The two atoms are said to *polarize* each other. On an atomic scale this attraction is the same as the attraction of a neutral object, perhaps a pith ball, to a charged rod, as seen in an elementary laboratory demonstration (Figure 24). The charged rod attracts the negative charges on the ball and repels the positive charges. After this separation the unlike charge is nearer, hence the net force is attractive. On the atomic scale the process is mutual, and the polarization is

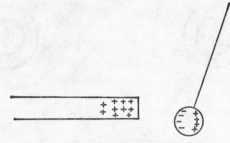

Fig. 24. Positive charge on rod repels positive charge on neutral ball, separating it from ball's negative charge. Since the ball's negative charge then is nearer the rod there is a net attractive force between rod and ball.

shared by both atoms. It should be noted that there is a clear distinction between this type of attraction and the attraction which binds together the two atoms of oxygen in the O_2 molecule previously discussed. When the two oxygen atoms came together they did indeed polarize one another at first, but the polarization increased more and more until some electrons on each atom synchronized their orbits and finally a few of the electrons began to swirl back and forth between the two atoms. No such synchronization occurs between the electrons on the two atoms of argon shown in the figure. The polarization activities are random and result in only a very weak attractive force between the atoms. If more than two atoms of argon are brought together a crystal is slowly built up. This solid is not very stable, and can be formed only at low temperatures ($-189°$ C) when the molecules are not vibrating strongly enough to shake loose from the weak force that holds them together.

A very large number of chemical compounds and several elements form these molecular-type crystals.[5] In one element, helium, the forces are so weak that no crystal can form except under considerable pressure and at the very lowest temperature; that is, below $4°$ Kelvin.[6] Most organic crystals are formed of organic molecules attracting one another by these weak polarization forces. Figure 8 shows the structure of a naphthalene crystal. Benzene, anthracene, and innumerable other molecules are able to form these molecular-type crystals. The fundamental question is: How well bound are the electrons in the molecule? If they are arranged in closed shells, as in the rare gas atoms, they will not take part in exchanges with other atoms and molecules, and the weak polarization activity alone results in forces holding the structure together. In the case of some molecules the closed shell condition is not as simple as the eight-electron condition of the argon atom. In N_2 five electrons from each atom can form very stable orbits which will not be disturbed by other N_2 molecules. Similarly,

[5] Even when the unit of a crystal is a single atom, as in argon, the crystal is customarily called a molecular crystal. It really should be called an atomic crystal in these few cases.

[6] On the Kelvin scale the freezing point of water is $273°$. See *Near Zero* by D. K. C. MacDonald (Science Study Series S 20).

stable orbits are formed between the six electrons
of each oxygen atom in an O_2 molecule. A solid
oxygen crystal is formed in which the molecules
are bound together with the same polarization
forces which bind together the molecules of a
nitrogen crystal, argon crystal, or benzene crystal.

4. *Diamond-like Crystals*

The atoms of carbon, silicon, and germanium
cannot form crystals in the ways crystals of ions
or crystals of molecules are formed. The carbon
atom has four outer electrons (Figure 18) and
it cannot make a closed ring of eight by giving
up or by collecting four more electrons. If it gave
up four, it would have such a strong positive
charge of plus four units that some electrons
would be recaptured instantly. If it tried to form
a closed shell of eight, the extra four electrons
would give it such a strong negative charge that
the shell of eight would explode and some electrons be driven off. Also, it does not form stable
molecules of C_2, as N_2 formed stable molecules, for another carbon atom brought near
would make C_3, all equally bound; another, C_4,
etc. This is the crux of the situation. Any number of carbon atoms can be added together to
form one molecule. Call it C_{1075} or anything you
like. A million carbon atoms stuck together in a
diamond is one molecule; a tiny flake of graphite
can be one molecule of carbon, too.

In crystalline nitrogen the electrons behaved
almost as they would on a free nitrogen mole-

cule. In NaCl crystals the electrons around the sodium ions and the chlorine ions are moving in approximately the same orbits as they would if the Na^+ or Cl^- ions were completely isolated. In carbon crystals the situation is very different. In empty space the electrons around a carbon atom move in much the same way as in any other free atom. But when carbon atoms come together and electron sharing occurs, the electrons move in very different orbits. All four of the outer electrons take part in the sharing with other atoms. All four electron orbits are synchronized with the motion of another electron on each of four other atoms. This very intense cooperation between two neighboring atoms results in the formation of a bond in which two electrons swirl back and forth between the two atoms encircling both. This behavior is very different from the behavior of electrons in a free isolated atom. It is, however, much the same as the behavior of those few electrons which participated in the bond between nitrogen atoms in the nitrogen molecule and the bond between oxygen atoms in the oxygen molecule. In the case of carbon all four electrons participate in bonding, making four bonds with four other carbon atoms, each of which has bonds to still more carbon atoms, etc. Each carbon atom is thus surrounded by four other atoms arranged in a tetrahedron (Figure 25). The combination of these arrangements results in the crystal structure we saw for diamond in Figure 12.

It should be pointed out that this remarkable

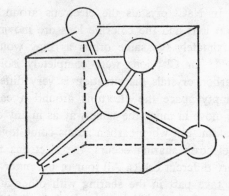

Fig. 25. The tetrahedral arrangement of bonds found in diamond, silicon, and germanium crystals. Four of these units make the diamond structure shown in *Fig. 12.*

property of carbon, that of being able to add similar atoms endlessly, allows it to be the basis of the huge molecules that are characteristic of organic materials, and of life itself. The bonds between each carbon-carbon pair are very strong, and even a molecule as long as a gene in chromosomes does not break up easily under normal biological conditions.

In ionic crystals and in molecular crystals any particular electron belongs to some ion or molecule and there it stays. In diamond the electrons are free to wander throughout the entire crystal. (In a formal sense they are confined to one molecule but then the entire crystal is one molecule. This is not very confining!) What is the path of one electron? It may be imagined binding two

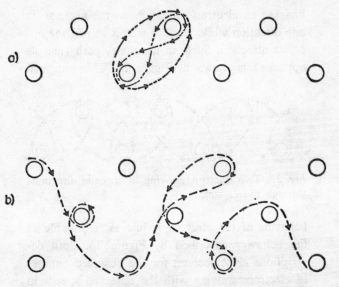

Fig. 26. Possible paths an electron in diamond might take: (a) encircling two atoms only, and (b) wandering throughout the crystal.

carbon atoms together (Figure 26a) by encircling them ceaselessly. Equally well it may be imagined making a zigzag path around one carbon atom after another and seldom repeating a visit to any one atom (Figure 26b). There is no way of knowing which path an electron follows. An experiment can say how fast an electron is moving, and in what direction, or where it is at some particular moment, but no experiment can follow the same electron from atom to atom. For some purposes (for example, discussing electric current in germanium) it is more convenient to imagine an electron's moving, on the average, in one direction while another moves in just the opposite direction. Such an imaginary path (and its opposite) is shown in Figure 27. This imagined

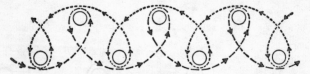

Fig. 27. Two electrons moving in opposite directions through the crystal.

behavior of the electron is just as reasonable as the behavior described by Figure 26. Both descriptions must account for the observed number of electrons moving with the observed speeds in the bonds and around the nuclei of the carbon atoms. In silicon and germanium the motion of the outer four electrons is like that described for diamond.

There is one important and startling thing that makes the electrons in a diamond-type crystal different from electrons in ionic and molecular crystals. Each electron in the process of bonding carbon atoms together can travel throughout the entire crystal and orbit around each atom. A monkey swinging from tree to tree is not half so busy as an electron swinging around one atom after another. In a diamond containing bonds between 10^{22} carbon atoms, every bond has two electrons all the time. Yet the electrons come and

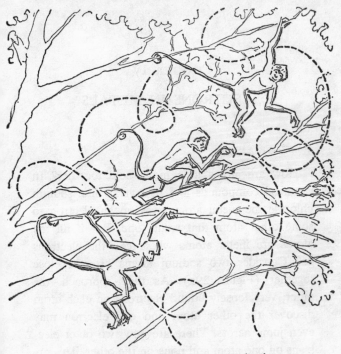

Fig. 28. Monkey orbits—no organization.

go continuously. In each bond and around each atom the electron orbits are so synchronized that one electron arrives just as another electron leaves. This is perpetual organization as well as perpetual motion.

CHAPTER IV

ELECTRONS IN METALS

1. *Electron Soup*

How are atoms in a metal held together? In chemical compounds and in crystals like sodium chloride the metal atom gives up an electron to some other atom that wants one. But if all the atoms are metal atoms where can the electrons go? Consider two sodium atoms brought close together (Figure 29a). As they approach, the outer, very loosely bound electrons on each atom discover the other atom and one electron may even jump across. There are now two outer electrons on one atom and none on the other. This arrangement is not at all stable and one or even both electrons may jump back to the other atom. For the short time that the two electrons were near one atom, that atom may be regarded as a negative sodium ion, Na^-, which attracts the other positive sodium ion, Na^+. Thus, two sodium atoms can be weakly bound together because of the high mobility of their outer electron.

If two more sodium atoms are brought close to the first two (Figure 29b) there are now four loose electrons wandering around the four atoms.

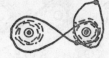

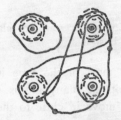

Fig. 29. (a) Two atoms of sodium. Only the outer electron of each atom is shown. The inner shells of electrons are represented by the dashed paths. (b) Four sodium atoms, with outer electron of each shown.

The electrons repel one another and so all four will never be found on one atom while the other three atoms are bare. For brief moments, however, one atom may have two electrons and it will then be negative and will attract the positive sodium ions near it. As more atoms are added to the group it becomes harder to say just which atom has which electron. The electron path becomes more like that shown in Figure 30. For a definite part of its travels the electron may appear to belong to one atom (for example, the completely encircled atom marked *A* in the fig-

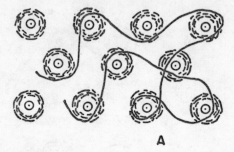

A

Fig. 30. Sodium crystal. For clarity, only one electron path is shown.

ure), but most of the time it merely skirts the outer orbits of many atoms. The electron does not often move in close to the centers of atoms. It was originally an outer electron of one atom and seldom moved in close to the center of that atom. While these electrons and other electrons are moving mainly in paths between the atoms, as shown in the figure, they are attracted to, and themselves attract, the positive sodium ions near them. Thus, the outer single electrons from each sodium ion together form a kind of "soup" of negative charge in which are floating the positive Na^+ ions. The negative "soup" attracting the positive sodium ions holds the sodium metal together.

This fluid electron soup accounts for the ability of all metals to conduct electric currents easily. When an electric field is applied to a metal by connecting the metal to a battery, the fast-moving electrons tend to drift along through the metal in the direction the battery forces them to move. Electrons are supplied at one end by the battery and are removed at the other. Similarly the fact that metals are good conductors of heat is due to this electron "soup"—or electron "gas" as most physicists call it. If one end of a metal is heated the electrons of the soup start moving somewhat faster. These faster electrons carry their excess energy—the kinetic energy[1] of $\frac{1}{2}mv^2$ due to their speed—to other parts of the metal, which then becomes hot.

There is another interesting property of this electron soup which holds the metal together. The "soup" holds the metal ions together almost as well in the liquid state as it does in the solid state. It acts as a fluid in which the ions can move around in the liquid state or in which the ions can form a regular pattern, the crystalline metal. Compare the electron orbits in sodium and diamond (Figures 30 and 27). Sodium melts at 97° Centigrade, just below the temperature of boiling water. This is a low temperature compared with the melting points of most elements. Although it takes only a little heat to break up the crystal and make it liquid, the ions cannot be released from the soup until much more heat is

[1] Energy is the ability to do work. The work a moving body can perform when being brought to rest is called *kinetic energy* and is equal to $\frac{1}{2}mv^2$, where m is the mass of the body and v its velocity. The *potential energy* of a body is its capability of doing work by virtue of its position and is equal to the amount of work that has been done against gravity or other force to move the body to its position.

applied. Sodium must be heated to nearly 900° C to evaporate. In diamond, on the other hand, the electrons are in very definite bonds and have none of the "soupy" property of the electrons in sodium. To melt diamond sufficient heat must be applied to loosen the bonds. These bonds are so strong that the crystal must be heated above 3500° C to break them. Once the bonds are broken the atoms simply evaporate from the crystal without forming a liquid. The wide temperature range of the liquid state is characteristic of many metals. Almost everyone is familiar with the common liquid metal, mercury.

There are other metals like iron, tungsten, etc., which have higher melting points. These metals are held together by two separate methods—the electron "soup" which we have just discussed and bonds between individual atoms as in the diamond lattice. These metals thus have the strength property of the rigid bonds and the electrical property of the electron soup.

2. *Electrons Are All Different*

Electrons are strange particles. They all behave differently. Although every electron is like every other electron as far as its mass and its charge are concerned, no two electrons are ever found in the same place, moving the same way, at the same time. When two electrons are close to one another they will always be found moving at different speeds or moving in different directions, or, if they have the same speed and direction, they may be orbiting around different atoms. (There is yet another way in which two electrons can behave differently. Each electron spins about its own center like a tiny top. The direction of the axis of this spin can be different from one electron to another.)

The need of every electron to be different from all other electrons results in very interesting behavior. We might facetiously compare it with the behavior of stylish women who devote much time and effort to finding clothes unlike anyone else's. If they should miscalculate and two of them appear on the same day in identical hats, these two women would not be found going along the same street together. Either one would be moving at a much greater speed than the other or one would change direction and go along the other

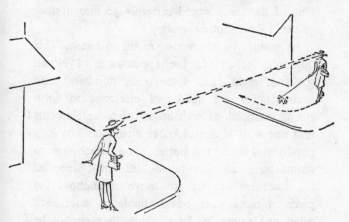

Fig. 31. The differentness principle applied to the behavior of ladies of fashion.

side of the street or even along a different street. Similarly with electrons. They rearrange their "orbits" and paths so that they are all different.

This "differentness" principle, known as *Pauli's Exclusion Principle,* is of fundamental importance in all atomic systems. As we have seen (Chapter III), eight electrons form closed and very stable groups orbiting around a nuclei of atoms. Why eight? Because in the world of electrons around atoms there are eight ways of finding orbits that are only slightly different. A ninth electron is one too many and it must go into quite a different orbit . . . or quite a different activity. Similarly we may imagine our two well-dressed ladies walking along, one on each side of the street. If a third appeared with a hat the same as the other two, that is just too many for the street. One of the three would certainly go into a store or turn off on another street.

In atoms the electrons are all different. This difference results in the appearance of closed shells of eight (and some other numbers) and accounts for the ability of electrons to form strong connections with atoms of some elements and not with atoms of other elements. But in a good metal where the electrons are detached from atoms how can they be all different? Since all the electrons are free to move throughout the piece of metal each one is liable to meet each other one sooner or later. Thus, they cannot be different in the sense of being located at different places. Their differentness must be in speed and direction of motion.

First, let us discuss how different the electrons are in an imaginary one-dimensional metal. Think of a narrow tube 7.2 centimeters (nearly 3 inches) long, as shown in Figure 32. Into this

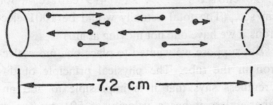

|←——————— 7.2 cm ———————→|

Fig. 32. Small tube 7.2 cm long containing a few electrons. No two electrons have the same velocity.

tube we place electrons one at a time. The walls of the tube are imagined to be so close that only lengthwise motion is possible. In this imaginary situation it is known just how different the electrons must be. No two electrons in the tube can have velocities within one cm/sec of each other.[2] If one electron is moving with a velocity of 10 cm/sec the nearest velocity any other electron can have is 9 cm/sec or 11 cm/sec in the same direction. If we want to place 1000 electrons in this small tube as efficiently as nature would —that is, with the least possible effort or energy— we must give the electrons the smallest possible

[2] The length of the tube was chosen to make the velocities simple numbers. If the length had been chosen as one centimeter the velocities would be multiples of 7.2 cm/sec.

velocities. We would then have 500 electrons
moving to the left with velocities given negative
values, and 500 electrons moving to the right
with velocities given positive values. Each electron would have a different velocity, ranging
through the values −500 cm/sec, −499 cm/sec,
−498 cm/sec . . . . +499 cm/sec, +500
cm/sec. (The total actually would be 1001 electrons if we have one not moving at all.)

But suppose we wanted to place one more electron in the tube. The physical principle of differentness says that it is impossible to add another unless it has a velocity of 501 cm/sec or
greater. If we did put one extra electron in the
tube with a velocity of 550 cm/sec, then each
time this electron hit anything it could (and probably would) lose some energy until its speed
would be reduced to 501 cm/sec. After slowing
to 501 cm/sec the electron cannot lose more
energy, for it then would be the "same" as some
other electron. This never happens.

Now let us make a list of all electron velocities
allowed in a cube of approximately 7.2 centimeters on a side, just as we did for the one-
dimensional tube of the figure. The list must be
a three-dimensional one because the electrons
can have a component of velocity in the x, y, and
z directions simultaneously. The differentness
condition (Exclusion Principle) is that no two
electrons have the same components of velocity
in x, y, and z directions. Since the cube is ap-

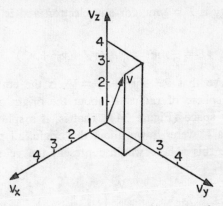

Fig. 33. Arrow marked v denotes a velocity. The amount that this arrow extends in the x direction is called the x component and is written v_x. Similarly v_y and v_z are the amounts that v extends in the y and z directions. Here we see that $v_x = 1$ cm/sec, $v_y = 2$ cm/sec, and $v_z = 4$ cm/sec.

proximately 7.2 centimeters on the side the velocities must be separated by 1 cm/sec in each x, y, and z direction. The simplest way to insure that all velocities are at least 1 cm/sec different from all other velocities is to plot the points representing velocity on a three-dimensional velocity graph (called velocity space) as is done in Figure 34. The list of all possible velocities is then a complete three-dimensional network of all these points. As can be seen from the figure, there is no point closer than 1 cm/sec to any other point.

What is the effect of trying to place electrons in the cube with the least possible energy as we did for the small tube in Figure 32? The kinetic energy is $E = \frac{1}{2}mv^2$ for any electron and is equal to

$$E = \frac{1}{2}mv^2 = \frac{1}{2}m(v_x^2 + v_y^2 + v_z^2)$$

Observe that $v_x^2 + v_y^2 + v_z^2 = V^2$ is the equation of a sphere of radius V about the origin of velocity space (Figure 34). That is, if a sphere of radius V were drawn about the origin, all points inside this sphere would represent the velocities

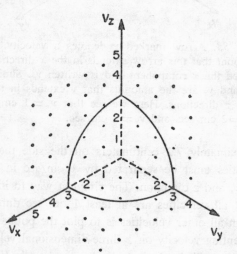

Fig. 34. Diagram showing allowed velocities for electrons in a 7.2 cm cube. For clarity, only points in the $v_x v_y$, $v_y v_z$, and $v_z v_x$ planes are shown. The points really fill all the space of this three-dimensional velocity graph, "velocity space." Also shown is a section of the sphere $v_x^2 + v_y^2 + v_z^2 = V^2$ where $V = 3$ cm/sec. All points inside the sphere correspond to electrons with lower kinetic energy than that of all points outside the sphere.

of certain electrons whose kinetic energies are all less than $E = \frac{1}{2}mV^2$, and all points outside the sphere correspond to electrons with greater energy than $\frac{1}{2}mV^2$. Thus, to give each electron its separate velocity and the least energy possible, nature will use up the points of velocity space with electrons in a spherical manner. When all the many electrons in our three-inch cube of metal have been accounted for, their velocities will fill all the points of velocity space up to a certain very large sphere and no more.

For a metal like copper the radius of this velocity sphere is 1.58×10^8 cm/sec and for sodium 1.07×10^8 cm/sec. This listing of all velocities is the same as saying that all points in velocity space with v less than 1.58×10^8 cm/sec (for example, in copper) correspond to the velocity of some electron in metal. Points outside the sphere correspond to a velocity greater than that possessed by any electron. Physicists say that points inside the sphere are "occupied." Points outside the sphere are "unoccupied." The boundary between occupied points and unoccupied points, which is spherical in this elementary picture, is called the *Fermi Surface*. Figure 35 shows the Fermi Sphere for sodium. Note especially that the velocities of the last few electrons are very large indeed—of the order of 10^8 cm/sec. This speed is within almost 1 percent of the velocity of light. Remember, the only reason for these large electron velocities is that the electrons themselves "know" what velocities other elec-

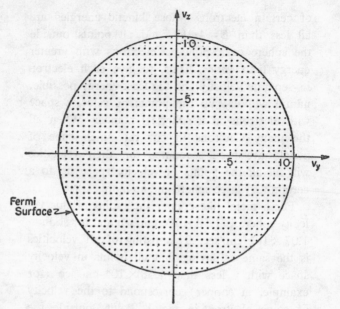

Fig. 35. Velocities of electrons in sodium. The maximum velocity (the radius of the sphere) is 10.7×10^7 cm/sec. Each point represents the y and z components of velocity of some electron. For clarity, only one point is shown for every five million in each direction.

trons have and do not take the same values. This is entirely the result of electrons all being different: Pauli's Exclusion Principle.

3. *Electron Reflections*

The reflection of X-rays is easy to understand. Whenever the wavelength of the X-ray beam fits exactly at some angle the atomic spacing in a crystal, the X-ray is scattered (Figure 14). This scattering, called *Bragg scattering,* was discussed in Chapter II. We also mentioned the startling fact that material particles seem to have a wavelength, as de Broglie correctly assumed. Just as X-rays are scattered so are electrons scattered, even in their motion inside the crystal, whenever their wavelength fits exactly some spacing of planes of atoms in the crystal. For material particles like electrons the wavelength depends upon their speed; the faster they move the shorter is the wavelength. That is, the wavelength, *L,* is inversely proportional to the velocity, *v:*

$$L = \frac{h}{mv}$$

The constant, *h,* Planck's constant,[3] is a universal constant of nature, and *m* is the mass of the particle. The velocities of electrons in a metal vary all the way from near zero to approximately 10^8 cm/sec. The higher velocity electrons have shorter wavelengths. How short?

$$L = \frac{h}{mv} = 7 \text{ Å } (= 7 \ 10^{-8} \text{ cm})$$

for an electron of 10^8 cm/sec velocity (Table II). In sodium metal the widest spacing of any plane is 3 Ångströms, as shown in Figure 36. Since all

[3] Formulae, like this one involving *h* ($h = 6.6 \ 10^{-27}$ erg sec), Planck's constant, are derived in the study of the mechanics of atoms and small bits (quanta) of energy. The physics of particles and quanta of energy is called quantum mechanics.

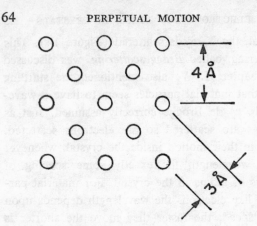

Fig. 36. The largest spacing between adjacent planes of atoms in sodium is 3 Å.

the electrons in sodium have wavelengths longer than

$$2 \times 3 \text{ Å} = 6 \text{ Å}$$

there will be no reflection of electrons in sodium metal. In other metals, however, there are usually more electrons and some of these electrons may be moving fast enough to have wavelengths sufficiently short to be reflected. In fact, this is the case for most metals. Sodium and the other alkali metals are the exception. One electron per atom usually does not "fill up" velocity space far enough for some electrons to reach velocities that can be reflected by atomic spacings.

Thus there are electrons within most metals with wavelengths short enough to be reflected by the crystal lattice, just as happens with X-rays. What effect has this on the electrons of the metal? It is most curious. The electrons are segregated into groups depending upon the wavelength. (See Table II.) Those electrons with wavelengths greater than the critical wavelength for reflection belong in one group and those with wavelengths less than the critical wavelength belong in some other group. Moreover, it is never easy (and is sometimes impossible) for an electron to move from one group to another.

TABLE II

Particle	Velocity	Wavelength
Slow electron	1 cm/sec	7.2 cm
Fast electron	10^8 cm/sec	7.2×10^{-8} cm* (7.2 Å)
Oxygen molecule in air	2×10^5 cm/sec	6×10^{-10} cm†
Proton shot from cyclotron	6×10^{-9} cm/sec	6×10^{-13} cm§

* Three times the size of atoms.
† Thirty times smaller than atoms.
§ Three times the size of nuclei.

Let us examine the behavior of one electron in a crystal. We choose to think of only one electron at the moment to eliminate the necessity for it to be different from all others. In Figure 37a we draw one electron moving slowly to the right with a speed and wavelength as shown. The vertical lines represent sheets of atoms which will cause reflection. Imagine that there is an electric field pulling the electron to the right, making it go faster. In Figure 37b the electron has speeded up and its wavelength shortened but not

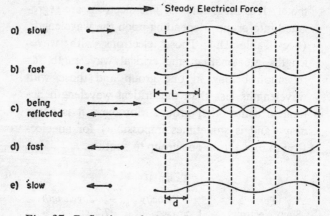

Fig. 37. Reflection of electron waves by planes of atoms (represented by vertical dashed lines). Reflection occurs when $L = 2d$.

yet enough for reflection. In Figure 37c the electron has just reached the velocity required to make its wavelength fit the distance between the sheets of atoms. Now it is reflected. In Figure 37d it is going in the opposite direction— that is, to the left, with about the same speed. Since the force of the constant electrical field is pulling the electron to the right it will slow down as in Figure 37e, stop, and then move toward the right, speeding up slowly until it is again reflected and starts the whole cycle once more.

What a strange situation! Although the electric field pulling the electron to the right is a constant and steady pull, the electron, under the influence of this force and of the atoms in the crystal, moves to the right and to the left oscillating back and forth. The reason is simple. As the electron gathers speed its wavelength changes and it is suddenly reflected. The electron can never move faster than a certain critical velocity or, said an another way, can never have its wavelength shorter than $2d$. All electrons that initially have speeds less than some critical speed will never[4] go faster than this. The electrons form a group by themselves or, in the language of crystal physics, a separate band.

What happens if the electron has a speed initially just above the critical speed? This situation is the same in principle as the last, and one reflection more complicated. An electron starting with such a velocity will also oscillate back and forth as shown in Figure 38. Start with the electron moving to the right and being pulled to the right in the electric field. Its speed increases and wavelength decreases until, as before, there is a fit between wavelength and spacing of the planes of the crystal. This fit occurs at the wavelength $L = d$, instead of $L = 2d$ as seen previously. The

---

[4] If the electric field pulling the electron is very large there is a slight chance that the electron will not be reflected but rather will continue to increase speed in the direction the force pulls it. The field must be very large since the electron has to gain a small amount of potential energy in order to cross the reflection speed. Also, if the electron is in a very strong magnetic field and its path consequently is curved, it may sometimes be hard to know just when the wavelength along a curved path "fits" the spacing of the planes of atoms. Thus, in a very strong electric or magnetic field some electrons do escape reflection.

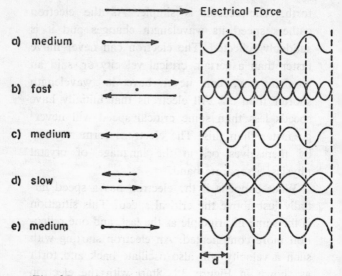

Fig. 38. Reflection of electrons by planes of atoms. The speed of the electron remains greater than v_c and less than $2v_c$. Reflections occur when $L = 2d$ and $L = d$.

critical speed is $2v_c$, just twice the previous critical speed. The electron is now reflected. We have drawn an arrow in both directions, for at this instant we cannot say truly in which direction it is moving. It ends up, however, moving to the left with a velocity nearly twice the critical velocity. The electron now slows down; the electric force is pulling it in the direction opposite to its motion. Its speed decreases and its wavelength increases until it is just the speed (v_c) and wavelength ($L = 2d$) to "fit" a lattice spacing again. Once more it is reflected. After reflection it is moving to the right with a speed just greater than the critical velocity, and we are back again to the starting point. This electron could not be made to move faster than twice the critical velocity, $2v_c$, nor slower than the critical velocity, v_c. It is in a band of speeds between v_c and $2v_c$.

As before, there is a small chance that the electron can cross the reflection velocity at $2v_c$ and go faster providing it can gain the small amount of potential energy which is required. This is not possible in normal situations in metals in the laboratory. Similarly, it could move more slowly than v_c provided it can give up the appropriate amount of potential energy.[5] Usually the electron cannot give up energy for another reason. It

[5] The small amount of potential energy required to cross the critical velocity arises in an interesting way from the wave nature of the electron. (The kinetic energy, $\frac{1}{2}mv^2$, is not involved since it changes smoothly as v goes through v_c.) As the electron increases speed approaching $v = v_c$, the wavelength shrinks approaching $L = 2d$. Right at $v = v_c$ and $L = 2d$ there are two extreme potential energies the electron can have. These two extremes are shown in Figure 39. The lowest energy situation is Figure 39a, which occurs when the loops of the wave are nearest the atoms in the crystal lattice. This is the nearest the negative charge of the electron wave can approach the positive ions of the crystal, and hence it is the lowest possible energy. The other extreme is obtained by moving the electron wave along a quarter wavelength. Now the electron negative charge is farthest away from the positive ions and work must be done to get it there. This extra work is the chunk of potential energy the electron must obtain to cross the critical velocity barriers. If this energy is not available the electron will certainly be reflected.

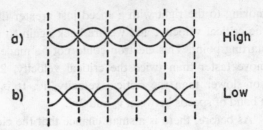

Fig. 39. Position of wave loops with respect to atoms in crystal lattice determines potential energy and probability of reflection.

would then have the same speed as some other electron. But the electrons must be all different and this differentness condition may prevent an electron's crossing over one of the critical reflection velocities.

There is also a band of speeds between $2v_c$ and $3v_c$, and so on. The electrons in each band are reflected when they otherwise would be ready to cross over one of the critical velocity lines. Figure 40 summarizes the velocities available in each band. The dotted lines show the reflections discussed for the first two bands.

In a real three-dimensional metal electrons are also reflected. The situation is not very different from the simple one-dimensional picture. Whenever the x component of velocity reaches v_c, the x component alone is reflected. Similarly for the y and z components. There is an important difference between three dimensions and the one-dimensional situation previously discussed. The critical velocity now is different in different

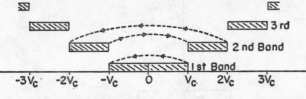

Velocity of Electrons

Fig. 40. Schematic drawing shows the range of velocities available to an electron in each of several bands. The dotted lines indicate the reflections discussed for the first band in *Fig. 37* and for the second band in *Fig. 38*. The critical velocity v_c, is the lowest velocity at which an electron can be reflected: the wavelength of the electron must be $L = 2d$.

directions. Figure 41 illustrates this. Suppose that the critical velocity in both the x- and y-directions is v_c. It could turn out then that any electron whose velocity can be represented by an arrow lying within the square cannot be reflected. That is, the electron whose velocity is represented by the length of the arrow, A, cannot be reflected even though its speed is greater than v_c, the critical velocity in the x- and y-directions. The sides of the square define the critical velocities in other directions.

In three dimensions the surface of a solid figure defines the critical velocity. For sodium the solid figure is shown in Plate X. The sphere inside the solid represents the sphere of all the electron velocities in sodium, the Fermi Sphere. We see that no electron in sodium reaches the critical velocity. However, if sodium had more

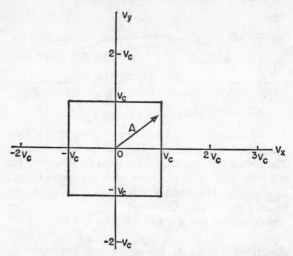

Fig. 41. The critical velocity for reflection in two dimensions is defined by the sides of the square.

electrons, the Fermi Sphere would be larger and could touch the faces of the dodecahedron. Some electrons could then be reflected by planes of atoms in the crystal and other electrons could not be reflected.

Most metals have more electrons than sodium. The behavior of these electrons can be very complicated and difficult to understand. Unraveling the activities of electrons in metals has been a major field of research for many years. The subject promises to remain interesting, and in part mystifying, for many years to come. Man's understanding of the behavior of electrons, though very great, still cannot predict such a commonplace useful quantity as the resistance of a copper wire.

CHAPTER V

ELECTRICAL CONDUCTIVITY

1. *Metals: Obstacles in the Soup*

The action of the electron pictured in Figures 37 and 38 is really very strange. There is a constant electrical force pulling it to the right, yet the electron spends the same time moving to the left as to the right. It gets nowhere. This looks like an easy way of getting alternating current from a battery. Of course, it isn't. The description we have given is of an ideal situation. It doesn't really exist any more than a mechanical machine without friction exists. For a flow of electrons in a crystal there is also a kind of friction. This friction is the scattering of electrons when they meet some obstacle in their path.

In a real metal, electrons encounter many obstacles which tend to scatter them from the direction in which they are moving. If an electric field is applied the electrons cannot increase speed continuously as we imagined for the ideal situation in the last chapter. Sooner or later, they make a collision with some obstacle in the crystal. In fact, we should say "sooner" rather than "later" for in a piece of wire at room temperature an electron may be scattered 10^{15} times per second.

However, it probably flies past a hundred atoms between each collision—an immense distance in the world of electrons.

The obstacles doing the scattering may be atoms out of line with the rest of the row of atoms, gaps in the line where atoms should be but are missing, other kinds of atoms included in the crystal by error or intentionally, and all other cracks, irregularities, and departures from perfect crystal structure. Figure 42 is a schematic

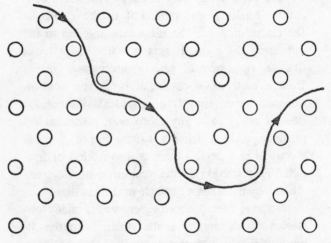

Fig. 42. Schematic sketch of an electron being scattered where an atom is missing from the lattice.

drawing of an electron being scattered by one of those defects from perfect structure, a missing atom. Although the electron can navigate through the rows of atoms if the atoms are in good order, the lack of even one atom from a place where it should be may cause scattering.

Other obstacles cause scattering in much the same way. As long as the crystal structure is perfectly regular, the electron path curves and bends around each atom in turn and continues on, in the same direction, without hindrance. However, as soon as some irregularity in the pattern occurs there is a chance—it does not always happen—that an electron going by will be scattered. As always the scattering is possible only if the differentness principle is obeyed. The electron must still be different from all other electrons after it is scattered, just as it was before the scattering took place. This differentness condition has very important results in the scattering of electrons. An electron cannot decrease speed in being scattered because it would then have the same velocity as some other electron. Also, it cannot increase speed (and hence energy) unless there is a supply of energy available to it from outside. The differentness requirement thus reduces greatly the chance of an electron's being scattered when it meets some irregularity in the lattice. If scattering occurs at all it can only change the direction of the electron. A physicist would say that *the electron can be scattered only if its velocities before and after scattering lie on the Fermi Surface.*

Now, consider what happens when a piece of metal is connected to a battery. We say an electric current flows. How does this happen? When the battery is connected to a wire an electric force is applied to all the electrons in that wire. All electrons then tend to move in the direction of the force. If an electron is going to the right initially and the force pulls it to the right then it will try to go to the right even faster (Figure 43a). If it is going to the left (Figure 43b) the electric

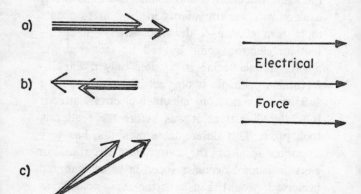

Fig. 43. Electrons tend to move to the right under the influence of the electrical force of the battery. The light arrow is the velocity of an electron before the battery is switched on. The heavy arrow shows the velocity of the same electron after the battery has been on for a short time.

force will tend to slow it down. If it is going in some other direction (Figure 43c), the electric force will tend to deflect it, making it travel more to the right. This tendency for all electrons to move to the right will have the result that all the points in velocity space will start to move a little to the right of their normal positions. Figure 44 shows this situation. The electric force is the same on all electrons, so their acceleration

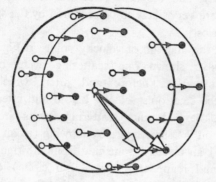

Fig. 44. The light and heavy arrows indicate the velocity of an electron before and after the battery is turned on. Only the tips of other arrows are shown as open and filled circles. All velocity points move uniformly to the right, so the whole Fermi Sphere moves.

is the same. Therefore all points in Figure 44 remain distributed throughout a sphere as they were before. But notice what has happened. There are now many points out beyond the original sphere (the Fermi Sphere) on the right-hand side, and there is a corresponding lack of points inside the Fermi Sphere on the left-hand side. This shift in the velocities of the electrons allows scattering to occur much more readily, for previously (without the battery) the differentness principle prevented such scattering. There were so few velocities of the same energy available that scattering could not often occur. Now there is an enormous number of velocities available (the vacated velocity points on the left-hand side of the Fermi Sphere), and the faster electrons moving to the right are very likely to be scattered by the various obstacles.

On the diagram of velocity points in Figure 45 we have shown one scattering event by the arrows marked "before" and "after," which indicate the electron's velocity before and after scattering. Several other scattering events are indicated on the same figure by showing (as an empty circle) an electron vanishing from the right-hand side and reappearing (as a full circle) on the left-hand side. It is easy to see that the farther the velocity points move to the right the more scattering of electrons can occur. In equilibrium the points moving steadily to the right under the force of the battery (Figure 44) equal the points moving to the left by scattering (Figure 45). In this steady condition there are slightly more points to the right; therefore, more electrons are moving to the right than to the left and so a net current is observed flowing in the wire. It is easy to estimate how far the sphere moves. This is just the average velocity of electrons in a wire carrying a current. Let us take a copper wire, 1 mm by 1 mm cross-section area, carrying 10 amperes. The current of 10 amps is the quantity of electricity flowing past any point in the wire at the rate of 10 coulombs each second. A coulomb is $0.62 \ 10^{19}$ electrons, and so out of the end of the wire are flowing $6.2 \ 10^{19}$ electrons every sec-

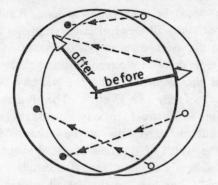

Fig. 45. Scattering of electrons moves the velocity points from the right side back to the unoccupied points on the left side of the Fermi Sphere.

ond. Now we must calculate what volume of wire contains this number of electrons. Then we can say that all the electrons in that particular volume move out the end of the wire every second. Copper has a density of 8.9 gms/cm³, and one atom weighs $64 \times 1.67 \ 10^{-24}$ gms. Thus there are

$$\frac{8.9 \text{ gms/cm}^3}{64 \times 1.67 \ 10^{-24} \text{ gms/atom}} = 8.4 \ 10^{22} \text{ atoms/cm}^3$$

Each atom of copper gives one electron to the "soup"; thus the density of electrons is also 8.4 10^{22} electrons/cm³. Ten amperes is 6.2 10^{19} electrons per second. Thus all the electrons in

$$\frac{6.2 \ 10^{19} \text{ el}}{8.4 \ 10^{22} \text{ el/cm}^3} = 0.75 \ 10^{-3} \text{ cm}^3$$

leave the wire every second. This volume of metal with the cross section of the wire 1 mm by

1 mm would be 0.75 10^{-1} cm long. Finally we say that since all these electrons move out each second the average velocity is 0.75 mm/sec. The average velocity of electrons drifting through the wire is tiny compared with the velocity ($\sim 10^8$ cm/sec) of any one electron. The displacement of points in Figure 44 is very much exaggerated. The shift in the velocity of the electrons is less than the width of the line in the drawing. The small shift shows how easily electrons can be scattered. They have no time at all to gain speed in the direction of the electric force before some obstacle deflects them.

Each time a fast electron from the right-hand side of the diagram is scattered to an available velocity on the left it not only changes direction completely but also loses a little speed. The loss of speed corresponds to a small loss in the kinetic energy of the electron. The lost energy is received by the atom or obstacle which did the scattering, and we observe the energy ultimately as heating of the wire carrying the electric current. Red-hot wire in electrical heaters, light bulbs, vacuum tubes, and electrical stoves are familiar to all, but we seldom realize that this heat comes from electrons gaining a small amount of extra energy and then losing it again in a collision with some obstacle in the wire.

It is especially interesting to notice that the velocities of the electrons themselves are almost identical either with or without the wire's being connected to a battery. The battery gives a very small amount of extra speed to the electrons. This extra speed allows some of the electrons to be scattered whereas previously their need to be "different" from all others prevented such scattering. On being scattered the electrons give up their very small amount of extra energy to the obstacle doing the scattering and thus heat the wire. If ever the electrons could suddenly put up with being the same as one another they could have very many more collisions and quickly stop their high-speed motion. If this happened the wire would not just glow red-hot, it might evaporate.

2. *Nonmetals: No Soup*

Insulators do not conduct electricity. This is, of course, why some materials are called insulators. The reason they do not conduct is a simple one. The electrons in most of these materials are tightly bound to some particular atom, ion, or molecule. In NaCl, for example, we saw that all electrons were orbiting around either the sodium ion, Na^+, or around the chloride ion, Cl^-. In a crystal of solid nitrogen, N_2, every electron belonged to some particular nitrogen molecule. They did not jump from one nitrogen molecule to another. The same is true of anthracene. Each electron belongs to some particular anthracene molecule and is not normally free to migrate through the lattice. Since all these materials have their electrons bound in one place and since these electrons are unable to move easily, no electric current will flow when a battery is connected. If the voltage of a battery connected to an insulating crystal is high enough, however, some electricity will flow through the crystal. But this is not normal conduction. This flow of electrons is more like a million sparks flying between adjacent molecules or atoms in the crystal. It is not conduction of electricity in the usual sense.

Diamond also is an insulating crystal. We saw in Chapter III that the electrons in diamonds move throughout the entire crystal and are not bound to any particular atom as in other insulators. Cannot these electrons flow through the crystal and thus be conducting an electric current? The answer is yes. Certainly, moving electrons constitute current. But every bond of diamond has two electrons coming and going in opposite directions simultaneously. Thus all currents are exactly canceled. If we place a diamond in an electric field which wants to move electrons to the right, as we did in considering electrons in a metal, the electric field will have almost no effect on the electrons in the diamond. The electrons would like to move to the right as they did in the metal, but no electron can move to the right unless some move to the left in each bond. The entire structure of diamond is like one huge molecule. All the bonds between atoms are complete, or saturated. This means simply that no more electrons can participate in the particular orbits which bond the crystal together. It is the same as saying that eight electrons in an outer shell of neon, Ne, or chloride ion, Cl^-, saturate that shell. That is, there are only eight ways of being slightly different and participating in the orbits of one shell. Similarly, in diamond there are only two ways per bond between carbon atoms for two electrons to be different and to participate in the bond. This saturation is just another facet of the differentness principle.

Without suggesting that much science is to be gleaned from the pages of *Vogue* or *Harper's Bazaar,* or from observing stylish women, nonetheless we can imagine a similar effect in their behavior. Suppose these women all agreed with one another (they wouldn't ever really, but electrons do) as to just how different they had to be in the hat line. Suppose they agreed that one hat per block each way was the minimum separation or differentness consistent with chic. (They would have to be on opposite sides of the street, of course.) If there were only a few identical hats in the shopping district, most of the time the ladies could walk where they pleased without suffering the indignity of meeting another identical hat. But as more and more of these hatted ladies went downtown to shop, they would have to be more and more careful not to pass another hatted lady, except on the other side of the street. Eventually as more and more ladies appear there would come a time when the downtown area had one such lady walking each way every block. This situation is saturation, as any woman will testify.

Note the consequences of saturation. One

woman wants to turn off the street she is on and go down a different one. But that street already has all the hats it can carry. If she wishes to remain respectably different she cannot turn! In diamonds the electrons cannot go the direction the electrical force would urge them because they must remain different from all others.

There is a way out for a determined lady with gumption. She can catch a cab, drive wherever she wishes, and still maintain her dignity and dif-

Fig. 46. Escape from saturation.

ferentness. In an atom with a closed shell of eight electrons another electron can be added provided it goes into another orbit or shell. In diamond an electron can be removed (with difficulty) from a bond and moved to another atom, but it cannot then form bonds with other electrons. It is as free to move throughout the diamond as the lady in the taxi would be to move throughout the downtown area. This extra electron can cause electrical conductivity. Normally, however, there is no extra electron, and so diamond is an insulator.

In silicon and germanium the same process can occur more easily. It requires much less energy to remove an electron from a bond and let it go wandering through the crystal. In fact, the energy required can often come from the vibration of the atoms in the crystal. Pure silicon and germanium are therefore not good conductors like metals but are *semiconductors*. Higher temperatures make the atoms vibrate more, and more electrons are torn from bonds and set free to conduct a current. The higher the temperature, the better is the conductivity or the less is the electrical resistance of silicon and germanium (Figure 47). The reverse is true in metals. At higher temperatures the atoms do indeed vibrate more strongly, but in a metal all possible electrons are already available for conductivity. Atomic vibration merely scatters electrons and thus increases resistance.

There is another method of making silicon and germanium conducting. A few atoms of the

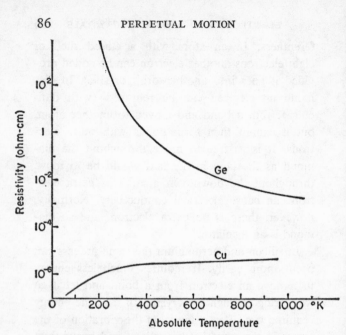

Fig. 47. Resistivity of copper and germanium as a function of temperature.

neighboring elements in the Periodic Table (Figure 16) can be grown into the lattice in place of a germanium or silicon atom. The atom of phosphorus, P, grown into the crystal would provide five electrons instead of four. Four of these form bonds with the surrounding silicon atoms, but the fifth electron is almost completely free to wander through the lattice. Figure 48 shows the extra electron orbiting at a distance around its own phosphorus atom. It is so loosely bound that a small force or the vibration of an atom can free it and set it wandering throughout the crystal. On

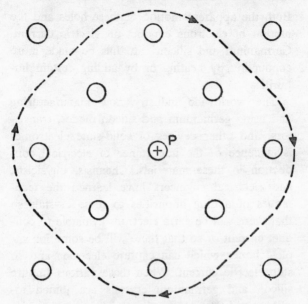

Fig. 48. Schematic diagram of the orbit of an extra electron around the positive phosphorus impurity in silicon. (All the other electrons—two per bond—have been omitted.) The extra electron can be pulled away from the phosphorus impurity. It is then able to conduct electric current.

the other hand, if an aluminum atom with three outer electrons were added to a silicon crystal there would be a deficiency of electrons. Some bonds could have only one electron. If an electron from a nearby bond moves into the unsaturated bond it would leave some other bond half empty. In this manner the empty bond can move from atom to atom. Physicists call the motion of half-filled bonds a current of positive "holes."

Both the apparent motion of these holes and the motion of electrons conduct an electric current. Germanium and silicon can thus be made more conducting by heating or by adding certain impurities.

The worldwide industry now manufacturing and using germanium and silicon diodes, transistors, and other devices of solid-state electronics is evidence of the importance of electrical conduction in these materials. Chemists, physicists, and electrical engineers have learned the techniques of adding impurities to these crystals so that there will be extra electrons available to conduct current or so that there will be some incomplete bonds which can capture electrons and so stop electric current. When these various impure silicon and germanium crystals are joined together, different electronic devices can be made which control quickly and easily the flow of electric current. The modern electronics industry owes much to this special kind of perpetual activity.

Chapter VI

ATOMIC VIBRATIONS, FORCES BETWEEN ATOMS AND SOUND

1. *Electrons and Atoms: Perpetual Motion*

Electrons are perpetually moving. They whirl ceaselessly around the ions of ionic crystals. In diamond-like materials they seem to swoop around each atom in turn, visiting all the appropriate atoms in their highly organized orbits, which mesh like gears of a perfect machine. In metals the perpetual motion of electrons seems chaotic but in fact it also is highly regulated by the electron's need to be different.

Systems of electrons are true marvels of nature. Electrons are perpetually moving at very high speeds. They may travel one hundred times as fast as an earth satellite (that is, around the earth once every minute). And they are highly organized so that each one has a different orbit or a different velocity. In the head of a pin there are billions of billions of electrons, all ceaselessly moving, all acting differently from one another. It is really presumptuous of us to compare any system of electrons with man's feeble attempt to make a perpetual motion machine. There seems little chance that man can ever create such a beautifully planned system.

Electron motion is not the only type of perpetual movement in crystals. The atoms themselves vibrate back and forth forever. The distance the atoms move and their speeds are both very small compared with the electrons' motions. In the first place, atoms do not go far. They move at most about $\frac{1}{20}$ of the distance to their nearest neighbors in the crystal and then move back again. This is negligible compared to the long flight of an electron in metals. Secondly, in the time it takes an atom to move this small distance, about 10^{-12} seconds, an electron can have traveled past several thousand atoms. The speeds of atoms only seem small, however, when compared with speeds of electrons. They are large enough in man's scale of motion. Atoms in crystals have speeds of vibratory motion like the speeds of gas molecules—that is, a fraction of one mile per second.

What causes the atoms to move back and forth? For that matter, when atoms in a gas collide why do they bounce apart again? The answer to both questions is the same. We know that atoms are not really solid balls bouncing off one another but electron clouds around nuclei which give the same effect. Figure 49 is a sketch of two atoms in collision. The nuclei of the atoms never get close, for as soon as the cloud of electrons around each nucleus starts to interpenetrate,

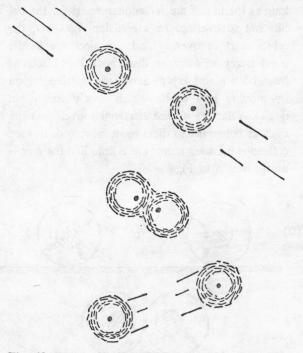

Fig. 49. Two atoms in collision. The electron clouds prevent the heavy nuclei from approaching very closely in terms of atomic distances.

these clouds themselves become much disturbed, perhaps as at the center of Figure 49. This disturbance is a result of forces between electrons. These forces are of two kinds. First, the electrons repel one another because they all have like (negative) charges. Second, the differentness of electrons is an important factor. Two electrons can have like orbits on two different atoms as

long as the atoms are far enough apart for the orbits not to overlap. In a collision, however, the
orbits start to overlap and the electrons in the
overlap region become disturbed. The electrons
from both atoms try to avoid the overlap region
by moving into orbits which barely touch but
don't overlap. If all the electrons move, then the
nucleus belonging to them must move too. In fact,
collisions between atoms are a little like the mechanism drawn in Figure 50.

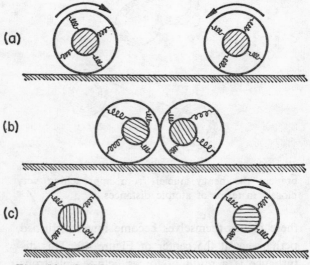

Fig. 50. Collision of two ping-pong balls with
spring-supported lead centers.

Imagine two ping-pong balls with a lead marble tied in the center with tiny springs. When
the two balls collide, the shell of the ping-pong

ball stops on contact and the heavy lead center continues to move a little until the springs stop it. Then the lead recoils on the springs and the balls roll apart again. This picture is a trifle exaggerated because the electron cloud is fuzzy, not sharp like the edge of a ping-pong ball, and some overlap is necessary. Also, the electron clouds distort a little as the ping-pong ball would if it were more flexible. This crude picture is useful, however, in that we learn that the mass of the atoms, the nuclei, never approach one another. Only the light outer shells of the electrons come into contact and cause the nuclei to recoil in a collision.

In a molecule or in a crystal the atoms seem to be in contact with one another continually. Any motion of one atom immediately causes a repulsive force from its nearest neighbor. This force prevents free motion and restricts the atom to vibrating back and forth about its average position. The situation is somewhat like Figure 51. The atom shells have been omitted in this schematic drawing, and we imagine that the little springs are joining each nucleus directly to its neighbors. Suppose the other atoms are clamped in position and A is given a push in some direction. It will continue to oscillate back and forth forever. This is indeed perpetual motion, but it is no more interesting than a pendulum or a weight bouncing up and down on a spring. Both of these would vibrate up and down or from side to side forever if there were no friction in our

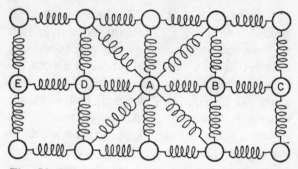

Fig. 51. The simplified concept of springs holding atoms in position in a crystal. Many diagonal springs have been omitted.

world, as in the world of atoms. The interesting thing about the motion of atoms in crystals is not so much its perpetual property, but rather the way the motion of one atom makes its neighbors move.

In Figure 51 the atoms around *A* are not really clamped. If *A* moves toward *B*, *B* pushes it back and is also itself pushed toward *C*. Similarly *D* is pulled in the direction of *A* and, in turn, tries to pull *E*. Any motion of *A* will cause its neighbors to move a little. The motion of any atom influences all other atoms in the crystal. As a result of this mutual influence the perpetual motion of atoms in crystals is highly organized, just as was the motion of electrons. But the reason is different. There is no direct application of Pauli's Exclusion Principle for atoms. Only the forces connecting every atom to its neighbors cause this high degree of organization.

2. *Elasticity and Oscillation*

There is a simple way to estimate the size of the forces that make atoms vibrate. If the forces were tiny springs, as in Figure 51, all that would be required would be to stretch the springs and measure the force. It is true that there is no way to attach hooks to the two atoms *A* and *B,* pull them apart, and measure the force and the distance stretched. But if a hook is attached to millions of little springs simultaneously the force is large enough to measure. This experiment is shown in Figure 52. If the wire is of steel and

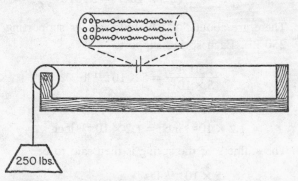

Fig. 52. Experiment to measure stiffness of tiny springs connecting the atoms of *Fig. 51.*

$\frac{1}{32}$ inch in diameter, a 250-pound weight will make a 3-foot length of wire stretch $\frac{1}{4}$ inch. Since the stretch is uniform every piece of the wire must stretch $\frac{1/4}{36} = 0.007$, or almost 1 percent of its length. So also the distance between neighboring atoms must change 1 percent.

But, how many tiny springs have shared the 250-lb load? This also may be estimated. The distance between atoms is about 3×10^{-8} cm, which equals approximately 1.2×10^{-8} inch. Therefore, if the wire diameter is $\frac{1}{32}$ of an inch ($= .03$ inch) there are

$$\frac{0.03 \text{ in}}{1.2 \times 10^{-8} \text{ in/atom}} = 2.5 \times 10^6 \text{ atoms}$$

across the wire diameter. Thus the number of atoms exposed on the end of the wire is approximately

$$\frac{\pi}{4} D^2 = \frac{\pi}{4} (2.5 \times 10^6)^2 = 5 \times 10^{12}$$

There are about 5×10^{12} little springs supporting 250 lbs. Each spring supports

$$\frac{250 \text{ lbs}}{5 \times 10^{12}} = 5 \times 10^{-11} \text{ lb}$$

It stretches 1 percent of

$$1.2 \times 10^{-8} \text{ inch} = 1.2 \times 10^{-10} \text{ inch}.$$

The stiffness of the spring is then said to be

$$\frac{5 \times 10^{-11} \text{ lbs}}{1.2 \times 10^{-10} \text{ in}} = 0.4 \text{ lb/in}$$

Of course, these small atomic forces would break long before they stretched an inch, but if they didn't break it would require 0.4 lb to stretch one inch—quite a stiff little spring.

If a spring of this stiffness is attached to a weight as shown in Figure 53 the weight will vibrate when disturbed. If the weight is one pound

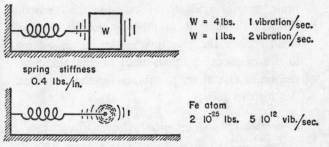

W = 4 lbs.   1 vibration/sec.
W = 1 lbs.   2 vibration/sec.

spring stiffness
0.4 lbs./in.

Fe atom
2 10^{25} lbs.   5 10^{12} vib./sec.

Fig. 53. The same spring causes different masses to vibrate with different frequencies.

the spring will cause two complete vibrations a second. If the weight is 4 lbs it will vibrate only once a second. If the weight is smaller the vibrations are faster. The formula for frequency of vibrations is

$$f = \frac{1}{2\pi} \sqrt{\frac{\text{stiffness}}{\text{mass}}}$$

If the mass has the weight of an iron atom $(2 \times 10^{-25}$ lb) the vibration frequency will be much higher.

$$f = \frac{1}{2\pi} \sqrt{\frac{0.4 \text{ lb/in} \times 12 \text{ in/ft}}{2 \times 10^{-25} \text{ lb/32 ft/sec}^2}}$$

$$= 5 \times 10^{12} \text{ vibrations/sec}$$

Thus, this little spring would make an atom of iron vibrate about 5×10^{12} times each second. This frequency is thousands of times faster than any mechanical system man has devised in the laboratory.

An atom by itself (as in Figure 53) must vibrate several million million times a second. When it is hooked to other atoms with these small springs the vibrating motion is passed on to the neighboring atoms until all the atoms of the entire crystal try to vibrate together, even at this high frequency.

3. *Sound Waves—Organized Atomic Vibrations*

How organized, we now ask, is atomic motion in crystals? The simplest situation in which organization of this vibrating motion can easily be seen is drawn in Figure 54. This is an imaginary

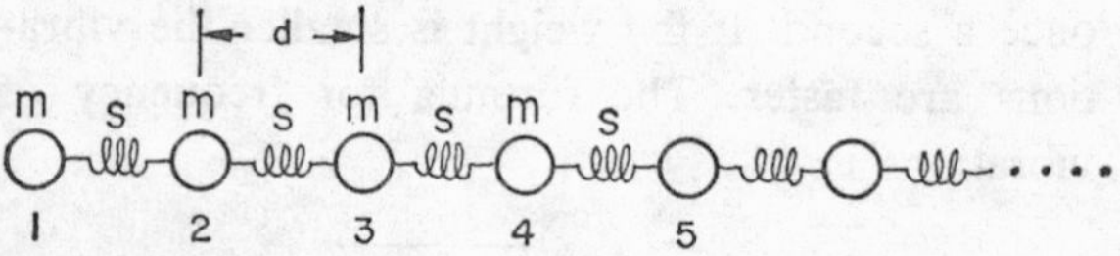

Fig. 54. Single row of atoms of mass m joined together with springs of stiffness s.

one-dimensional crystal with a single row of atoms of mass, m, tied together with springs of stiffness, s. Imagine what would happen if the end atom, No. 1, were moved quickly to the right and then back again. As it moves to the right it compresses the first spring, which moves the second atom, which compresses the second spring, and so on. Moving the first atom to the right moves each atom in succession a little bit to the right. Moving it back again will also move each atom in succession down the line. Notice that motion is transmitted from atom to atom down the chain.

Also, the heavier the atoms the slower the pushes will travel. The velocity of these pushes can be found in physics textbooks and is:

$$v = d \sqrt{\frac{s}{m}} \qquad \text{where}$$

s is the stiffness, d is the spacing between atoms, and m is the mass of the atoms. If the left-hand atom is moved slowly back and forth a few times it makes its neighbor vibrate back and forth with it and its neighbor's neighbor and so on. It produces a wave which travels down the line as a wave travels down a rope. This wave is a wave of vibration, a sound wave. It travels down the line with exactly the same speed as did the wave caused by a single push or pull.

If the left-hand atom is moved back and forth more rapidly than before, the atom next to it will start to vibrate back and forth at the same frequency as the first atom and the atom next to it and so on. The vibrational motion will propagate down the line. However, if the frequency is higher this time than previously the speed of propagation down the line is less! This is a remarkable fact about vibration in crystals. The speed of propagation of the vibration depends on the frequency of vibration. Such a result is a little unexpected because vibrations in air, like sound, all seem to travel at the same speed. The high and low notes of music travel at the same speed. If they didn't we would hear not music but discordant noise. In solids, however, at extremely high "sound" frequencies of some million million (10^{12}) vibrations per second, this is not the situation. Some vibrations travel faster than others.

It is easy to understand a simplified picture of why some vibrational waves or sound waves travel at different velocities. Imagine in Figure 54 that atom No. 1 is being vibrated back and forth quite slowly. Then the information about its motion travels down the line of atoms with the speed

$$v = d \sqrt{\frac{s}{m}}$$

and all the atoms move back and forth in turn, each one delayed a short time, $\frac{d}{v}$, from the one to its left. Now, if atom No. 1 is moved back and forth very quickly it may be already on its way back to its original position when atom No. 2 starts moving to the right. Hence, the force that 1 exerts on 2 is partly canceled. From the point of view of atom No. 2 it looks like a weaker force between them. Since s, the spring stiffness, appears to decrease, the velocity $v = d \sqrt{\frac{s}{m}}$ also decreases. This phenomenon is due solely to the fact that each atom must learn about its neighbor's motions before it can start to move. It is too complicated to write down the detailed arithmetic showing just how the velocity varies with frequency of vibration. The result of such a calculation for the chain of atoms is shown in Figure 55. Velocity is plotted along the ordinate and

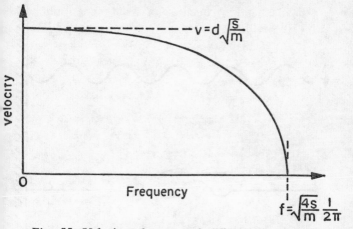

Fig. 55. Velocity of waves of different frequency along the chain of atoms of *Fig. 54.*

frequency along the abscissa. Note that as the frequency is increased the velocity decreases, slowly at first and then more rapidly, to zero velocity.

What is a zero velocity wave in a crystal? Vibrations in crystals are somewhat like the two situations shown for the rope in Figure 56. One shows a wave traveling down the rope. The other shows what is called a "standing wave"—that is, a wave with no velocity. In crystals the frequency at which the velocity goes to zero corresponds to the wavelength's being exactly two atomic spaces. A wavelength equal to two atomic spaces is the same condition as that required for reflection of X-rays (Chapter II) or electrons (Chapter IV). Zero velocity is, however, more than the waves' not knowing which way they are going

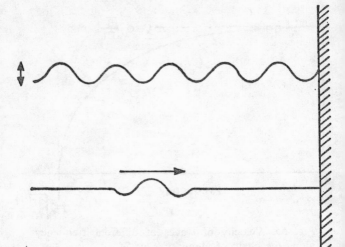

Fig. 56. A "standing" wave and a traveling wave on a rope. The standing wave does not appear to move to left or right.

because of reflection and re-reflection. For this vibrational wave it means also that atoms next to one another are always moving in opposite directions. Figure 57 shows this kind of motion. It is clear that there is no wave being propagated down the crystal because every second atom is following the same motion with no time lag. All

Fig. 57. Standing wave of atoms. One-half vibration later every atom is going in the opposite direction, and pairs that were close together are far apart.

atoms are vibrating simultaneously and to ask which way the wave is moving has no meaning.

If one atom is moved back and forth faster than the critical frequency where the velocity goes down to zero, only the atoms near the one being moved vibrate back and forth; they will move in a random manner, for the first atom is being moved too fast for the others to keep up. This random motion dies out in a distance of a few atom spaces, and no wave is sent down the line, nor is a wave sent through a real crystal. The frequency, f, at which the wave velocity becomes zero is thus the maximum frequency that can be sent through the crystal as a wave. For the one-dimensional crystal of a chain of atoms this frequency is given by

$$f = \frac{1}{2\pi}\sqrt{\frac{4s}{m}} = \frac{1}{\pi}\sqrt{\frac{s}{m}}$$

which is twice the frequency of an atom of mass, m, and spring of stiffness, s, vibrating alone (Figure 53).

If the atoms are not all alike the vibrations are more complex. Consider the chain in Figure 58 in which all springs are the same but two kinds of atoms alternate down the chain. This can be

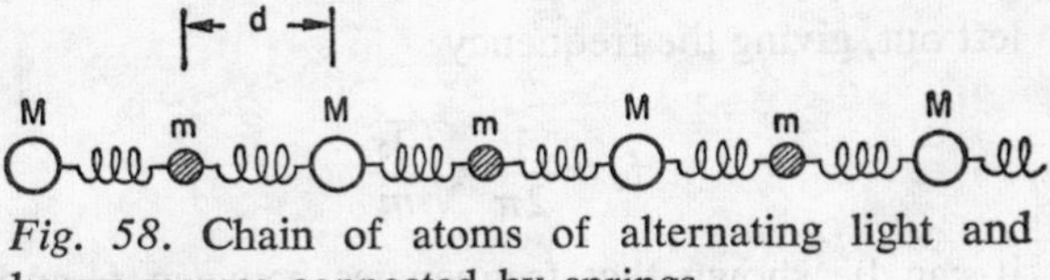

Fig. 58. Chain of atoms of alternating light and heavy masses connected by springs.

thought of as a line of atoms in an NaCl crystal. The light sodium ions are marked m and the heavy chloride ions M. The motions possible for this chain are more complicated and will not be discussed in detail. There are three different situations now for which the velocity is zero. Figure 59a, b, and c show these situations. Figure 59a

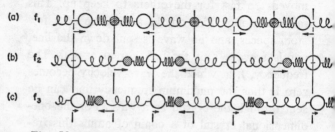

Fig. 59. The three possible standing waves on the "diatomic" chain of Fig. 58. The vertical lines indicate the equilibrium position of the atoms.

shows the light atoms not moving at all—these can be omitted. We have left a chain vibrating just as it was for the chain of Figure 58, giving the frequency

$$f_1 = \frac{1}{2\pi} \sqrt{\frac{2s}{M}}$$

Figure 59b is exactly the same except that now the heavy atoms are not moving. They can be left out, giving the frequency

$$f_2 = \frac{1}{2\pi} \sqrt{\frac{2s}{m}}$$

It can be shown that frequencies between f_1 and

f_2 cannot be propagated as waves down the chain. They die out as did frequencies above the critical frequency for the simple chain of light atoms. The third situation in which the velocity is zero is shown in Figure 59c. Note that here both masses are moving and the stationary point is some point of the spring between each pair of different atoms. Waves with frequencies between f_2 and f_3 do exist and travel through the crystal. A graph of velocity against frequency would now look like Figure 60. The interesting thing about

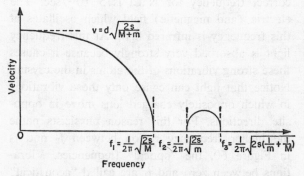

Fig. 60. Velocity of waves down the diatomic chain of *Fig. 58*. The three zero velocity waves of *Fig. 59* have the frequencies f_1, f_2, and f_3, as indicated.

this graph is that it is divided into two parts. In the region between O and f_1 the adjacent atoms, m and M, are always moving in the same direction; in the region between f_2 and f_3 they are always moving in opposite directions.

Suppose each heavy atom in the chain was the negative chloride ion, Cl^-, and the light atoms were the sodium ions, Na$^+$. When these oppositely charged ions move in opposite directions they set up an electric field. Or, conversely, an electric field can make these ions move. In an electric field all the positive ions (Na$^+$) move a little in the direction of the field and all the negative ions (Cl$^-$) move slightly in the opposite direction. If the electric field reverses its direction back and forth, at the correct frequency it can cause strong vibrations of this kind in which adjacent atoms move in opposite directions. The correct frequency for NaCl is 5 10^{12}/sec. The electric (and magnetic) field which oscillates at this frequency is infrared light. At this frequency light is absorbed very strongly because it causes these strong vibrations of the atoms in the crystal. Notice that light can cause only those vibrations in which oppositely charged ions move in opposite directions. For this reason physicists name the higher frequency region between f_2 and f_3 in Figure 60, the "optical" frequencies. Vibrations between zero and f_1 are called "acoustical" because sound wave frequencies are included in this region, very near the zero end.

4. *Measuring Forces between Atoms*

The forces between atoms in a crystal are really much more complex than the little springs with which we represent them in Figure 51. There is as yet no complete theory from which physicists can calculate all the vibrational frequencies and related properties of a crystal. Therefore, experi-

PLATE IX. Photograph of fluorite (CaF_2) crystals. The differences in color come from the addition of small amounts of impurity.

PLATE X. Scale model of the velocity distribution of electrons in sodium metal. Compare with *Fig. 35*. Any point within the sphere corresponds to the velocity of some electron in sodium. The solid figure around the sphere defines the "critical velocity" for reflection of an electron. It can be seen that all electrons in sodium are traveling too slowly for reflection.

PLATE XI. An apparatus for studying the velocities of electrons in metals. This experiment can measure the velocities of electrons in different directions in a crystal, and the results can be plotted in diagrams like *Fig. 35* and *Plate X*.

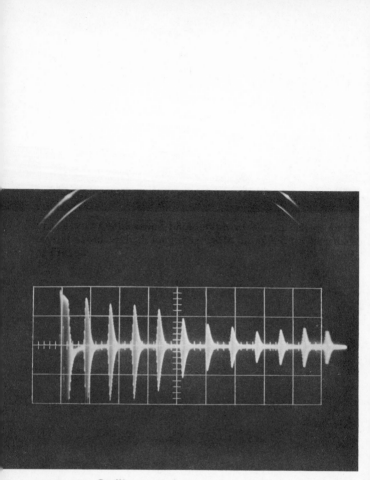

PLATE XII. Oscilloscope photograph of sound echoes in a crystal about ½ inch long taken with an apparatus like that of *Fig. 62*.

PLATE XIII. A cut-away view of a neutron spectrometer which measures the change in speed of neutrons scattered by vibrational waves in crystals. Neutrons of one speed are selected by the crystal M, scattered by the specimen at S, and have their new speed determined by the analyzer at A. The specimen and analyzer have been omitted from this sketch. ATOMIC ENERGY OF CANADA LTD.

PLATE XIV. A neutron spectrometer of the type sketched in *Plate XIII*. This one is installed at a reactor at the Chalk River Laboratories of Atomic Energy of Canada Ltd. As in the previous plate, neutrons of one speed are selected at M, scattered by the specimens S, and have their new speed measured by the analyzer A. ATOMIC ENERGY OF CANADA LTD.

PLATE XV. An apparatus for studying the magnetism of electrons in iron and other magnetic materials.

PLATE XVI. Photograph of a lead ring immersed in liquid helium carrying a supercurrent. The magnetic field of this current is strong enough to repel (and hence to support) the superconducting lead ball as long as the lead ball and lead ring are both kept at low temperature.

ARTHUR D. LITTLE CO., INC.

ments of many kinds are used to determine these properties. Two of these experimental methods have already been discussed. Simple stretching or compressing of a crystal (as was done for the wire of Figure 52) gives directly the values of the stiffness of some of the little springs. The second method discussed was the measurement of the frequency of light absorbed by a crystal like NaCl. This experiment gives the vibrational frequency and some information on the stiffness of the springs at this frequency. The most powerful technique for determining the forces between atoms is to measure the velocity of sound in a crystal. This velocity depends upon the stiffness of many of the tiny springs we imagined connecting the atoms.

The simplest method of measuring sound velocity would be to tap one end of a rod with a hammer and listen for the sound to arrive at the other end. Such an experiment is cartooned in Figure 61. The physicist on the receiving end has a stopwatch in hand, and he tries to measure the time for the blow to travel down the rod. However, sound travels so fast in a rod that he would do better to measure the velocity electronically. A quartz crystal glued to one end of the rod can be made to vibrate many times and then stopped. The vibrational wave will travel down the rod and then vibrate the crystal at the other end, giving an electrical signal. The time between the sending and receiving of this burst of vibrations can be measured on an oscilloscope, as

Fig. 61. Uncomfortable method of measuring sound velocity in a rod.

shown in Figure 62. Sound velocity measured in this way turns out to be several thousand meters (that is, a few miles) per second. These values of sound velocity can then be used to calculate spring stiffness. However, the highest frequency sound that modern techniques can generate and transmit through a crystal is about 10^9 per second.[1] This is still a thousand times less than the maximum frequency in most crystals. How can the spring stiffness at higher frequencies be measured?

The experimental method most useful in measuring velocity of higher frequency waves is both more complex and more interesting. The method has been used only recently, for it requires beams of neutrons available from uranium reac-

[1] Vibrational waves of this frequency are still called sound waves although the human ear hears nothing above 2×10^4/sec.

Quartz Crystals

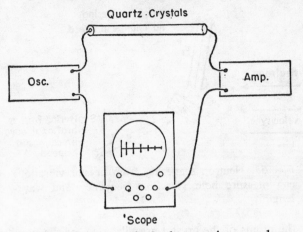

Fig. 62. Practical method of measuring sound velocity in a rod. The sound vibration is transmitted down the rod and picked up at the other end. The time of travel is measured electronically on the oscilloscope.

tors. The experiment consists of scattering neutrons from a crystal and measuring their change in direction and in speed. This experiment differs slightly from the diffraction of X-rays and neutrons discussed in Chapter II. Figure 63 illustrates the situation. If neutrons enter and leave with the same velocity v_1, they undergo ordinary diffraction and obey the Bragg law of reflection. Some neutrons, however, may change speed on being scattered, as shown in Figure 63. If the neutrons change their velocity from v_1 to v_2, the scattering process involves a vibrational wave of the lattice. In the scattering event the neutron may lose energy by increasing the amount that

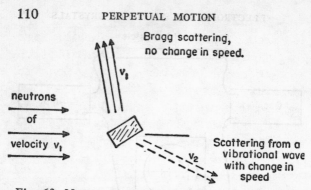

Fig. 63. Neutron scattering from crystal vibrations can measure both vibration frequency and wavelength.

the atoms of the crystal are vibrating, or the neutron may gain energy by decreasing the amount of vibration of some particular vibrational wave. The frequency of the vibrational wave scattering the neutron can be calculated from the change in kinetic energy of the neutron, using a simple formula.[2]

$$f = \frac{\text{K.E.}_{in} - \text{K.E.}_{out}}{h}$$

(If the neutron gained energy the sign of the right-hand side of the equation must be reversed.)

The wavelength of this vibrational wave can be obtained from the angle the neutron was scattered. It was shown in Chapter II that the angle of scattering could be used to determine the spacing of atom layers in a crystal. In this case, when

[2] See footnote, page 63.

the neutron changes its velocity as well, the angle of scattering can be used in very much the same way to determine the spacing of waves along one particular vibrational wave in the crystal. Thus from neutron scattering, physicists can measure directly both the wavelength and vibration frequency of waves moving through the crystal. The velocity of the waves can then be calculated from the product of frequency and wavelength, $v = f \times L$. This method of neutron scattering can be used to measure the frequency and velocity of vibrational waves over almost the entire velocity range of atomic vibrations. From these measurements the stiffness of the tiny springs, which we imagined connecting the atoms, can be determined. This neutron-scattering technique is easily the most powerful and most versatile of the methods physicists have available to study the motions of atoms in a crystal. A diagram and a photograph of a neutron spectrometer are shown in Plates XIII and XIV.

CHAPTER VII

ATOMIC VIBRATION, HEAT, AND HEAT CONDUCTION

1. *Vibrational Energy and Heat*

What causes the atoms in a crystal to vibrate? What is the origin of waves of vibration in a crystal? This question cannot be answered. It's much too difficult. To ask it is like asking why all nature is in perpetual motion, or, "Why is there motion in the universe?"

Some questions can be answered. When a crystal is placed on a hot stove or in a flame, the atoms vibrate much faster. Similarly, when placed on a block of ice the atoms vibrate more slowly. The mechanism is as follows. In a flame or other hot gas the molecules are moving very fast. When these molecules hit the side of a crystal a few atoms at the side of collision get a huge push. They in turn push their neighbors in the interior, just as in the chain of atoms with springs. A wave of vibrations passes into the crystal (Figure 64). The atoms in the top of a hot stove vibrate very strongly. If a crystal is placed on top of a hot stove, these atoms collide with atoms on the crystal surface next to them, and the atomic vibra-

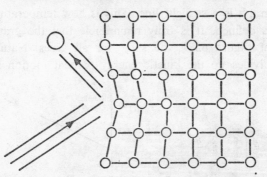

Fig. 64. Collision of a gas atom with a crystal causes vibrational waves to start through the crystal.

tions are passed on from one hot body to another.

The process works both ways. If the atoms in the crystal are vibrating very strongly, slowly moving gas atoms hitting the surface of the crystal probably will be bounced off with more speed (and thus energy) than when they hit. This transfer of kinetic energy of atoms from one material to another is called *heat flow*. Heat energy flows from the body with more kinetic energy (which is said to have a higher temperature) to a body with lower kinetic energy (lower temperature). Temperature is simply a measure of the average kinetic energy of a molecule in a gas. A hot gas is a gas in which the molecules are, on the average, fast moving. As a gas is cooled the average kinetic energy and speed of molecules decreases.

If the average kinetic energy of molecules in a gas is plotted against the temperature of a gas—measured in degrees Centigrade—a graph like Figure 65 is obtained. The upper portion of the graph is a straight line. This is how temperature is defined. It is truly remarkable that the graph of Figure 65 is the same for all gases. Nature divides up the kinetic energy of heat motion so

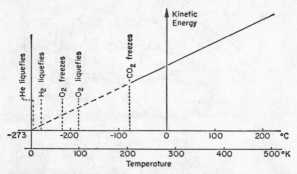

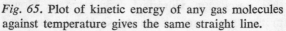

Fig. 65. Plot of kinetic energy of any gas molecules against temperature gives the same straight line.

that all kinds of molecules average the same energy. Since $E = \frac{1}{2}mv^2$, a heavy molecule like oxygen has an average lower speed than a light molecule like hydrogen. Since an oxygen molecule is sixteen times as heavy as a hydrogen molecule, the hydrogen molecule must then be moving four times faster on the average.

As the gas is cooled the straight line of Figure 65 is extended backward to negative temperatures. But finally it stops when the gas becomes a liquid or a solid. If it were extrapolated backward to still lower temperatures it would fall to zero kinetic energy at $-273°$ Centigrade. This temperature is called the *absolute zero*. At this temperature all the molecules in a gas would

stop. However, all gases become liquid or solid
before that low temperature is reached, so only
the molecules in an ideal imaginary gas would
stop. Even helium becomes liquid at $-269°$ C,
or $4°$ Kelvin as the absolute temperature scale
is called.

In a solid the motion of an atom is really very
similar. When a gas molecule hits the crystal
surface the collision sends waves of vibrations
into the interior of the crystal. The random motion of the gas molecules is converted into many
waves traveling throughout the crystal. If we
could see any one atom in a crystal it would appear to be moving in a random manner. Under
the influence of only one wave the motion would
look very regular. There are very many waves
moving the atom simultaneously in different directions. Each separate wave moves the atom at
a different speed and possibly in a different direction. The average speed is the result of innumerable vibrational waves setting the atom in
motion. It seems to be jiggling about completely
without order.

What is the kinetic energy of such a vibrating
atom? Again, nature is methodical in the presence
of so much random motion. The average kinetic
energy of the atoms in the crystal is the same as
the average kinetic energy of the molecules hitting the surface. Although the motion is limited
to vibrating back and forth and up and down,
*the kinetic energy, $\frac{1}{2}mv^2$, is on the average the
same as the kinetic energy of the gas molecules*

hitting the surface. When a gas is liquefied and then frozen into a crystal the atoms still have the kinetic energy of mechanical vibration they would have had if the gas had not condensed. The amount of perpetual motion of atoms depends only on temperature. Therefore, if the crystal is cold the atoms vibrate less and less in direct proportion to the temperature. Perhaps now the perpetual vibration can be stopped by cooling to absolute zero? But no, nature is not so simple. Motion does not cease. As the solid is cooled, the kinetic energy does not decrease as fast as it should. For crystals a graph of the kinetic energy plotted against temperature looks like Figure 66, rather than like Figure 65. All solids de-

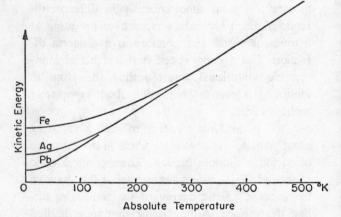

Fig. 66. The kinetic energy of atoms in a crystal is the same as for molecules of a gas except at low temperature. Atoms in a crystal do not stop vibrating even at absolute zero.

part from the simple straight line. *All crystals retain some kinetic energy even at zero degrees absolute.* The hard materials like diamond retain more energy than soft materials like lead.

There is no easy way to understand this residual motion at absolute zero. It is a result of the wave nature of matter and, like many other wave phenomena, is not easily grasped intuitively. The motion at absolute zero, however, is very real and can be detected in many experiments. This atomic vibration is truly perpetual. Not even cooling to absolute zero stops atomic motion.

2. *Sound Velocity and Heat Velocity*

The speed of sound waves in a crystal is very great, a few miles per second. The energy of sound waves is heat energy—that is, the energy of the vibrational motion of atoms in the crystal. Yet, heat certainly does not move with the great speed of sound. The basic reason is lack of perfection in crystals. Just as electrons in a metal cannot accelerate forever under the influence of an electric field, so sound waves cannot travel forever. They too are scattered by some obstacle. With sound waves, however, the scattering is harder to visualize because sound waves are often scattered by one another. The principle is the same. An electron (wave) or a sound wave is scattered by some departure from perfect alignment of atoms in an otherwise perfect crystal.

Suppose that a sound wave is moving to the right, as in Figure 67a. In the process of wave motion each atom gives a push to the next one in line. If the atoms are perfectly aligned the pushes will go on undiminished forever. Of course, the atoms are never really in line. They are vibrating continually from millions of other sound waves going by. Suppose that at some instance the

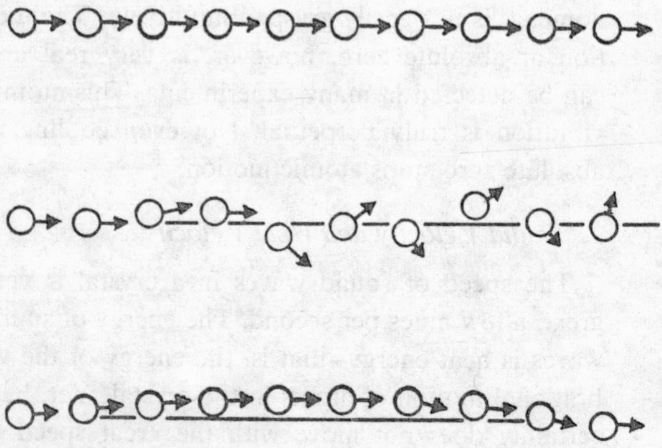

Fig. 67. (a) A wave of "pushes" moving down a well-aligned row of atoms. The little arrows show the motion of each atom. It must be remembered that the atoms move in turn one after another from left to right. Thus each atom should be imagined as moving the length of its arrow before the next atom moves. (b) If the atoms are badly out of line the "pushes" become disorganized quickly and cause atomic motion in other directions. (c) If the atoms are almost in line the pushes travel a long distance without disorganization.

atoms are displaced from their proper position as in Figure 67b. Now try to send along this line the same wave of pushes as was done in Figure

67a. The atoms probably will move in the direction of the arrows in the drawing. As the wave of pushes goes along the line it causes some atoms to move farther away from their proper position. At the same time the original component of push lying along the line gets less and less. The original push becomes lost after going only a short distance along this line. This is very different from the situation in a perfect line (Figure 67a) where the wave would go on undiminished.

Although the wave dies out, its energy is not lost. It is contained still in the kinetic energy of all the vibrating atoms along the line. Many of these atoms are not moving in the direction the first atom moved. The original wave thus dies out, and the disorganized motion of the atoms along the line moves other atoms in adjacent (not shown) lines, causing new waves to start off in other directions. These newly created waves in turn die out and create more waves. Before this happens many times, the original sense of direction down the line is completely lost, and the extra vibrational energy is diffused over a small volume of the crystal. In this small volume the atoms are vibrating somewhat more strongly than the atoms just around it. Thus, vibrational waves moving out of this small region are stronger than vibrational waves moving into this small region. This is the mechanism of heat transport.

Heat conductivity is the slow diffusion of the extra vibrational energy into a region where the vibrational waves are smaller. Here is the answer to the problem of heat velocity's being slower than sound velocity. Each little wave *does* move with the velocity of sound but it doesn't go far. It quickly dies out and creates other waves going in other directions. Hence, heat is conducted through a solid by a diffusion process which is much slower than the velocity of sound. The very long wavelength (low frequency) sound that can be manufactured in the laboratory does not indeed die out very quickly. Long wavelengths do not scatter other vibrational waves as much because the adjacent atoms are in almost perfect line. They are more like Figure 67c. Because most of the vibrations in a crystal are of very high frequency, much of the heat energy in a crystal is transported by waves that scatter easily.

The distance the higher frequency waves can travel is a subject of considerable research interest at the present time. Some measurements show that at ordinary temperatures the high frequency waves may travel a distance as short as a few atom spacings. Such motion is hardly wavelike. It is a tiny ripple.

3. *Heat Conductivity at Low Temperatures*

The heat conductivity of crystals changes greatly as the solid is cooled. It increases. When a crystal is cooled there are fewer vibrational waves to carry energy, and one would expect the heat conductivity to decrease. However, there is another effect which works the opposite way. As the crystal is cooled and the atoms vibrate less, many vibrational waves die out, but those remaining travel farther. The increase in the distance that the wave can travel more than compensates for the decrease in number of waves. Thus, the heat conductivity increases strongly, as shown in Figure 68. Eventually, at very low temperatures (about 40° K), the vibrational waves travel throughout the entire crystal. Now they can travel no farther and the conductivity falls to zero at the absolute zero because the number of waves available drops steadily to zero.

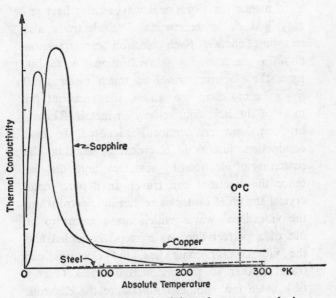

Fig. 68. The heat conductivity of pure crystals increases at low temperature to several times the value at room temperature.

Notice that at these low temperatures the conductivity of a perfect crystal of sapphire is as good as that of copper. The increase in distance that a vibration can travel certainly has a very strong influence on the crystal properties. In contrast with the conductivity in a good crystal, the conductivity of glass would be too small to show anywhere on Figure 68. Since the atoms in glass are not arranged in rows as in a good crystal, vibrational waves are never able to travel long distances, and glass is a poor conductor at all temperatures.

In metals the vibrational waves carry heat energy just as in nonmetals. But electrons also transport energy. Each electron can transport about as much energy as a vibrational wave, but since the electrons travel so much faster (100 times faster) than the waves, they account for most of the heat conductivity in metals. The vibrations, however, cannot be ignored. In heat conduction, just as in electrical conduction, the scattering of electrons by obstacles limits the distance the electrons can travel. In a pure metal crystal the chief obstacles scattering electrons are the vibrational waves which cause atoms to be out of a perfect line. As a metal is cooled and the vibrations become less, the electrons can travel farther so the conductivity rises (Figure 68). At a low enough temperature the electrons can travel completely across a small crystal, and at this temperature the conductivity reaches its

maximum. Further cooling reduces the energy
that can be carried by the electrons, and the conductivity falls to zero at the absolute zero. For
comparison, in Figure 68 is also shown the heat
conductivity of a very impure metal, steel. In this
specimen the electrons are scattered by built-in
obstacles, foreign atoms, and so the number of
scatterers does not change with temperature.
Thus, the conductivity falls slowly to zero as the
electrons are able to carry less and less energy.

The heat conductivity of all pure crystals,
metal and nonmetal, behaves much as sapphire
and copper behave, as shown in Figure 68. When
the temperature is lowered the motion of atoms
diminishes, and the distance a wave of vibration
or an electron can travel increases very rapidly.
Only the size of the crystal limits the distance.
In a large, perfect crystal at low temperature heat
would appear to travel with a velocity approaching the velocity of sound.

On the other hand, in an alloy like steel,
which is an iron crystal with many extra atoms
of carbon, manganese, and chromium, electrons
are scattered by such impurities. The conductivity
is poor at all temperatures. Similarly, in glass the
atoms are not arranged in good order (Figure 9),
and so vibrational waves cannot travel far at
any temperature. Thus the conductivity of fused
quartz, glass, and plastics is too small to be
plotted on the graph of Figure 68. This very
great difference in heat conductivity between good

crystals and disordered solids is only one result of the great degree of organization possible when the perpetually moving atoms and electrons of nature are arranged in long regular rows.

CHAPTER VIII

PERPETUAL MAGNETS AND CURRENTS

1. *Cooperation between Electrons*

A gas of carbon atoms is a chaotic affair. The atoms fly in all directions while at the same time the four outer electrons of each atom buzz around their own nucleus. When carbon gas is solidified into diamond, a very large amount of the chaos is replaced by a beautiful order. The atoms are now vibrating back and forth about their positions with almost the same speed as in the gas, but the four electrons of each atom are behaving altogether differently. Instead of circling around one atom as in the gas, they are now orbiting around all the atoms in a multitude of perfectly synchronized orbits. The electrons cooperate in the formation of orbits as soon as the temperature is low enough that the vibration of the atoms does not interfere. Raising the temperature gives atoms more vibrational kinetic energy. At a high enough temperature the kinetic energy is sufficient to destroy the cooperative orbits of the electrons and to remove an atom from the surface. This is evaporation of the atoms of the crystal.

The melting and boiling of matter are the two most familiar examples of the thwarting of cooperative activity of electrons by the violent motion of vibrating atoms. Two less commonplace examples of electron cooperation are (i) the permanent magnetism of iron and some other elements, and (ii) the phenomenon called *superconductivity,* the ability of some metals when cooled sufficiently to conduct an electric current without resistance.

2. *Permanent Magnets*

An electron, in addition to carrying one unit of electric charge, possesses a tiny bit of magnetism. Each electron behaves like a small bar magnet having a north and a south pole. Such a magnet tends to line up with any magnetic field. Within a filled shell of eight electrons there are four pairs of electrons, each electron in the pair canceling the other's magnetic field. A complete shell of eight electrons might look something like Figure 69. If, however, the number of electrons

Fig. 69. Schematic drawing of a neon atom showing the magnetic effects of electrons canceling in pairs.

in a shell is odd then all the little magnets cannot be canceled and the atom itself will show magnetic properties.

Iron atoms behave something like this even though there is an even number of electrons. The shell of electrons of the iron atom in metallic iron crystals is not complete. It has some unpaired electrons. These unpaired electrons influence the electrons in neighboring atoms as they orbit round and round. In the region where the electron orbits of the two atoms overlap, the electrons repel one another because of like charge. Secondly they repel or attract a little depending on whether their small magnets are parallel or antiparallel. Thirdly (and this is always a very important way the electrons influence one another) they must be different. The Pauli Principle states that electrons will avoid being like one another at the same time and same place. In the region between the atoms where the orbits overlap, one electron from each atom can even swap orbits and go around the other atom. This ability to swap orbits and the requirement of differentness force the electrons on one atom to cooperate with the electrons of neighboring atoms. In iron the result of this cooperation is that the tiny magnets of the unpaired electrons on each atom line up parallel to one another, as drawn schematically in Figure 70a. This situation is called *ferromagnetism*. The cooperation between electrons on neighboring atoms allows iron to become a permanent magnet.

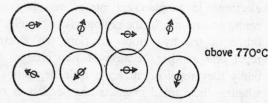

Fig. 70. Schematic drawing of atoms in an iron crystal. The little arrows indicate the direction of the magnetization of the unpaired electrons of each atom. Ferromagnetism is destroyed by the vigorous vibration of atoms at high temperatures.

In other crystals the electrons may find an easier (involving less energy) mode of cooperation. In iron oxide, FeO, for example, the electrons or alternate iron atoms are aligned in one direction, and the in-between atoms in the opposite direction. This situation is called *antiferromagnetism*. FeO is truly magnetic although no external magnetic field can be detected. All the magnetism is canceled out inside the crystal.

If iron, or iron oxide, or other cooperative perpetual magnets are heated the atoms vibrate more. When they vibrate strongly enough the electron shells overlap different amounts with each vibration. Cooperation between orbits of electrons on neighboring atoms becomes less effective until finally, at a high enough temperature, all cooperation breaks down. The ferromagnetism is lost. The electrons on adjacent atoms do not remain parallel but point in random directions. This happens if iron is heated to 770° K. The cooperation between electrons is broken by the violent vibrational motions of the atoms. Similarly, in FeO the electrons can no longer cooperate if the temperature goes above 198° K (−75° C). The temperature at which cooperative motion breaks down is a measure of the strength of this particular type of electron cooperative activity.

3. *Superconductivity*

Superconductivity is one of the most amazing examples of cooperation between the constantly moving electrons in a metal. It is also one of the weakest kinds of cooperation—that is, it occurs only at temperatures of a few degrees absolute. A very slight increase in atomic vibration beyond the zero temperature motion is enough to destroy the organization of superconducting electrons.

The resistance of a metal decreases with decreasing temperature, as shown in Figure 71. For certain metals a critical temperature is reached at which the resistance vanishes suddenly. This is *superconductivity*. Although this strange behavior of some metals was discovered in 1911, in

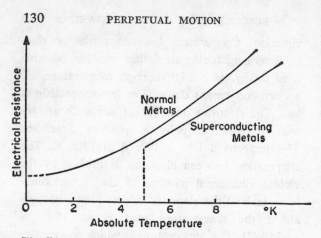

Fig. 71. At temperatures close to absolute zero some metals suddenly lose all electrical resistance. These metals are called superconductors. Pb and Al are superconductors; Cu is not.

Leiden, by Kamerlingh Onnes, many features of it are still not fully understood.

The effects of superconductivity are dramatic. An electric current, once started in a superconducting wire loop, will continue indefinitely. Plate XVI shows a photograph of a lead ring carrying an electric current continuously without external battery. The magnetic field created by this current can "float" the superconducting lead ball.

An unusual kind of cooperation between electrons seems to occur in these certain kinds of metals which are superconducting. An electron moving through the crystal somehow affects the atoms it passes in such a way that another electron can follow more easily. As other electrons follow along the path they maintain the "good" condition of the atoms along that path so that still more electrons can follow easily. The end result is a flowing of many electrons along special paths through the crystal. These electrons behave like marbles rolling along grooves in a board. They cannot be scattered out of the grooves unless enough energy is available to lift the marble over the side of its particular groove. Electrons cannot be scattered unless some energy is available to lift them out of their "groove." If they cannot be scattered, there is no electrical resistance. These electrons are perfect conductors—superconductors. The remarkable thing about superconductivity is that the grooves appear to be made by the electrons themselves. This is a co-operative adventure in which many electrons help each other to maintain a path along which to travel.

It is not yet fully understood what the electrons do to the atoms in the crystal to make this path. One possibility is that the conduction electrons

(a)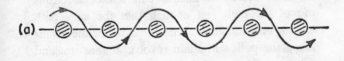

(b)

Fig. 72. The electron path in (b) is not quite as curved as in (a) because the atoms are pushed aside a small distance. Thus (b) might be considered the "easier" path for the electrons.

push the atoms a bit one way or another to make their paths easier (Figure 72). This path will, of course, be disturbed by heat vibrations. When the atoms vibrate strongly enough the electrons will be scattered out of the groove and the path will quickly deteriorate. The heat required is very little. For example, at 7.2° K lead loses its superconductivity and becomes normal. Mercury changes from superconducting to normal behavior at 4.15° K. Other examples are shown in Figure 73.

There probably are other ways the electrons can organize a path. Suppose that as a conduction electron went past an atom it encouraged some electrons of the metal atom to revolve in a certain direction. Then, if the electron did revolve in this direction another conduction electron might find it easier to follow this particular path. This kind of organization of the electrons on the atoms along the path resembles somewhat the organization causing ferromagnetism. Again, as the metal is heated vibrations can scatter electrons out of the path fast enough that the easy path cannot be maintained. The electrons of the atoms along the path will again revolve at random, and the material is no longer superconducting. Some such mechanism might cause superconductivity in vanadium which disappears when the metal is heated to 5.3° K. The details of this and other possible mechanisms causing superconductivity are not clear at the present time.

Many metals become superconducting at low

PERIODIC TABLE OF CHEMICAL ELEMENTS

SUPERCONDUCTORS SHOWN in ITALICS with TEMPERATURE of SUPERCONDUCTING TRANSITION

IA	IIA	IIIB	IVB	VB	VIB	VIIB	VIIIB			IB	IIB	IIIA	IVA	VA	VIA	VIIA	VIIIA
H (1)																	He (2)
Li (3)	Be (4)											B (5)	C (6)	N (7)	O (8)	F (9)	Ne (10)
Na (11)	Mg (12)											*Al* (13) 1.19°K	Si (14)	P (15)	S (16)	Cl (17)	A (18)
K (19)	Ca (20)	Sc (21)	*Ti* (22) 0.39°K	*V* (23) 5.3°K	Cr (24)	Mn (25)	Fe (26)	Co (27)	Ni (28)	Cu (29)	*Zn* (30) 0.88°K	*Ga* (31) 1.09°K	Ge (32)	As (33)	Se (34)	Br (35)	Kr (36)
Rb (37)	Sr (38)	Y (39)	*Zr* (40) 0.55°K	*Nb(Cb)* (41) 9.13°K	*Mo* (42) 0.92°K	*Tc* (43) 8.2°K	*Ru* (44) 0.49°K	Rh (45)	Pd (46)	Ag (47)	*Cd* (48) 0.56°K	*In* (49) 3.40°K	*Sn* (50) 3.72°K	Sb (51)	Te (52)	I (53)	Xe (54)
Cs (55)	Ba (56)	*La* (57) ~5°K	*Hf* (72) ?	*Ta* (73) 4.48°K	*W* (74) N0.01°K	*Re* (75) 1.70°K	*Os* (76) 0.66°K	*Ir* (77) .14°K	Pt (78)	Au (79)	*Hg* (80) 4.15°K	*Tl* (81) 2.38°K	*Pb* (82) 7.19°K	Bi (83)	Po (84)	At (85)	Rn(Em) (86)
Fr (87)	Ra (88)	Ac (89)	*Th* (90) 1.37°K	Pa (91)	*U* (92) 0.7°K												

* Ce (58), Pr (59), Nd (60), Pm (61), Sm (62), Eu (63), Gd (64), Tb (65), Dy (66), Ho (67), Er (68), Tm (69), Yb (70), Lu (71)

Fig. 73. Periodic Table of the elements showing which metals are known to be superconducting. The number beside the symbol for the element is the temperature (in degrees absolute) below which the metal is superconducting.

temperature. (The Periodic Table of Figure 73 shows all presently known superconductors.) Many other metals are known to remain normal even when cooled to very low temperatures. This startling difference in behavior between one metal and another is not yet fully understood although the problem is fifty years old. In addition to pure elements hundreds of alloys have been made that will carry perpetual currents. The number of such alloys is growing steadily as research in the subject of the perpetual motion of electrons progresses.

Chapter IX

THE CONTINUING SEARCH
FOR KNOWLEDGE

This brief survey has given a short glimpse of the motion of atoms and electrons in crystals. We have seen that the energy of vibrations of atoms in a crystal is the heat energy of that solid. We have learned of the remarkable way the motions of atoms in a crystal influence one another so strongly that they tend to vibrate together. We have talked about the ceaseless motion of electrons in crystals—from crystals of molecules with electrons bound each to its own molecule, to crystals of metals wherein some electrons are free to wander throughout the entire crystal.

Man's knowledge of these two areas of nature, born only fifty years ago, has grown at a tremendous rate in this last decade. Physicists and chemists are now measuring details of the motions of atoms and electrons in crystals with an accuracy not thought possible just a few years ago. Modern research is expanding man's knowledge at an incredible rate.

What is the use of all this research? Why do scientists want to know more and more of the secrets of nature?

There is a simple answer to the second question. Unraveling the ways of nature is one of man's most fascinating occupations. The contest between man's mind and nature's secrets—the unrelenting quest to understand the hows, the whys, the whens, of the natural world—is for many the ideal life. The only sure reward of this quest is the clearer understanding of some small part of nature, but to many dedicated scientists this reward is sufficient.

Many other scientists, engineers, and physicians are more concerned with making practical use of the already extensive knowledge of man and with pushing back the frontiers of knowledge in directions that promise immediate usefulness or relief from suffering. Their achievements are well known. Modern research has changed dramatically our health, by finding cures for many diseases; our clothing, by producing new textiles and other materials of common usefulness. It has increased our food supply; it has revolutionized world communication; and it has brought the excitement and pleasures of formal sport, music, and the arts to millions who otherwise would never have known them.

What particular contributions have resulted from knowledge of atoms and electrons in crystals? The most spectacular contribution is, of course, the transistor. The entire industry of solid-state electronics, which did not exist fifteen years ago, has grown out of the researches of physicists who studied the behavior of electrons and atoms in crystals, especially in silicon and germanium. The results of their research have led to a technology encompassing so much of modern electronics, from hearing aids to satellite communication, that the importance can hardly be estimated. The economic value has paid for all solid-state research for years to come!

Other scientists have produced many new materials, lighter and stronger than previously known, which are in present use in aircraft and satellites. The developments of metallurgy have resulted in metals which can endure the very high temperatures of turbine and jet engines. The engineer who measures the deflection of a bridge with a strain gauge is using a device of solid-state technology. The army sentry's infrared binoculars incorporate recent practical developments of solid-state physics. The future is certain to show many more products of our technological age.

But the question, "What is the use of all this research?" has not been answered. We have cited only examples of some research that has produced useful results. We have not faced the basic question: why pursue knowledge that is *not likely* to be useful? Before answering, let us first consider the close connection that exists between research for pure knowledge and research aimed at practical results. The principles of radio were demonstrated by Heinrich Hertz well before the turn of the century. But not until the Second World War were radio and radar developed intensively. After the war many scientists returned to university research and brought with them the modern electronic techniques. (This is applied physics helping the search for pure knowledge.) One of the results of their new skills was the detection of the magnetism of the atomic nucleus. This advance in pure knowledge is now used by geophysicists to measure the earth's magnetic field, thus helping to locate iron ore.

This multiple interdependence of pure knowledge and knowledge that can be gainfully employed is characteristic of all man's understanding of nature. No one can say with certainty that some particular area of knowledge is useless to mankind, although admittedly it is easy to anticipate that some areas will not be used in the immediate future. Knowledge of nature is a whole knowledge and does not come in two categories, useful and nonuseful. The utilitarian answer to the question, "Why research?" is that practical knowledge grows faster if a sufficient amount of pure knowledge grows with it.

There is a philosophic answer, too. Aside from direct usefulness, research, in the broadest sense, is as necessary to mankind as food. In order to live and grow, man must struggle and must succeed or fail. The great efforts which send astronauts into orbits, the scientist's search for true descriptions of nature's habits and laws, are necessary struggles. It is essential for all men that some individuals reach for the stars.

INDEX